EMF Freedom

Solutions for the 21st Century Pollution

3rd Edition

Breaking Away from the
MASS CONSciousness Series:
Insights Beyond Tunnel Vision

D1616436

Elizabeth Plourde, Ph.D.
Marcus Plourde, Ph.D.

Other titles by Elizabeth Plourde:

Sunscreens – Biohazard: Treat As Hazardous Waste

Sunscreens – Biohazard 2: Proof of Toxicity Keeps Piling Up

Sunscreens – Biohazard: Diet and Guide to Safe Sunning

Your Guide to Hysterectomy, Ovary Removal, & Hormone Replacement: What ALL Women Need to KNOW

Hysterectomy? The Best or Worst Thing that Ever Happened to Me? A Collection of Women's Personal Experiences

iv

Plourde, Elizabeth
Plourde, Marcus
EMF Freedom: Solutions for the 21st Century Pollution – 3rd Edition

ISBN-13:   978-0-9913688-3-9
LCCN: 2015913861

Cover design: New Voice Publications – Also see: Picture Credits

Published by: 21st Century Health Consulting LLC
                dba New Voice Publications
                publisher@newvoice.net
                Irvine, CA 92604

© New Voice Publications

Dedication

This book is dedicated to the growing number of millions of families whose lives have been drastically altered by electromagnetic fields (EMF) and toxic chemicals when their children were born with one of the autism spectrum disorders.

It is also dedicated to the millions of adult children who have had to become their parents' caregivers as Alzheimer's disease erased their parents' memories and are no longer recognized by them. Unfortunately, these adult children have to be constantly concerned about their parents safety and the safety of those around them.

In this 3rd edition, I have added an important group of people to whom this book is dedicated. Over the last 2 years, there has been an exponential growth in the numbers of people who are unable to function around electromagnetic radiation, a growth that parallels the growth in the numbers of wireless devices, cell towers, antennas, and Wi-Fi hot spots. Thousands are experiencing similar symptoms, expressing they are unable to be around computers, cell phones, Wi-Fi, and smart meters, to the point they can no longer work, and have to move out of their smart metered residences.

Dedicated to these canaries of this new electronic world and their families, may this book bring awareness that the proliferation of wireless devices needs to be reversed. We are electromagnetic beings and were not created to live in the 100s of man-made radiation frequencies that now permeate our world.

Acknowledgements

We want to thank all the researchers from around the world who have been working diligently to identify and convey the harm that electromagnetic radiation causes to life on the planet. Committed to preserving humanity's ability to survive, they are the brave pioneers of this new technological world, helping us understand that we cannot disrupt our body's exquisitely tuned electrical system without dire consequences. There are too many to individually list here, but some are listed throughout the book, resource list, and references. Please join us in recognizing their heroic contributions to protect us from the many disabling health conditions acknowledged throughout this book.

TABLE OF CONTENTS

Preface
1st Edition

My EMF Experience

My decision to research electromagnetic fields (EMF) came about when hearing so many complaints regarding insomnia and headaches after smart meters were installed in Northern California. Being a menopause practitioner, women were calling with these symptoms concerned they were going into early menopause. Hearing our electric company was preparing to install their new smart meters throughout our neighborhood, we opted out of having one installed on our home. We also had neighbors on one side expecting a child within weeks, and an elderly gentleman on the other side, who both opted out after hearing about the possible harmful effects. Because we did not have one and were protected on both sides of our house, I confidently felt I would not be impacted by the smart meter installations.

However, the meters started being installed in our neighborhood at the beginning of the week and by Thursday night an itchy rash developed around my ankle. Having had a long standing appointment with a doctor the following week, I thought she could determine what was causing it and tell me what to do for it. By the time I saw her the following Thursday, the rash was up my calf and covered half of my thigh. She stated it was not scabies and recommended herbs that help reduce skin inflammation.

Two weeks later, the rash was solid over my legs, arms, stomach and back. The itching was so intense, with nothing able to relieve it, there was no way to sleep. I felt like I was undergoing torture. I saw my primary care doctor, who stated it was probably scabies. When I said I had not been exposed to them, she prescribed cortisone cream and pills. This did not stop the spreading or the itching, so I was referred to a dermatologist who also stated it had to be scabies and prescribed scabies medication to be used over my total body.

Knowing it was not scabies, I chose not to use it. After several more weeks of being awake itching all night, I could not stand it anymore and went to another doctor who had helped me in the past. He thought it was a recurrence of the skin parasite schistosomiasis, which I had been infected with 30 years earlier. I underwent his schistosomiasis cleansing. After still being awake itching all night, I became desperate and utilized the scabies therapy 3 times, because the standard of applying it 2 times did not help. Still, nothing worked!

I was given referrals to an allergist (who's answer was: it was not contact dermatitis) and then to an infectious disease doctor (who's answer was: it had to be scabies). Finally, I was referred to the most highly regarded dermatologist in the area. His answer was to prescribe ultraviolet (UV) therapy treatments, stating that UV reduces skin inflammation.

By now, I could not use a cell phone or a computer due to itching, bloody sores breaking out up my arm and legs within minutes of using either device. My skin spontaneously started bleeding when I was exposed to any EMF radiation. It bled so profusely, many of my clothes and sheets were destroyed due to blood stains. Being a researcher and author, not being able to be around computers or cell phones meant I could no longer work. It was Christmas time and since some of the doctors were still convinced it was scabies, I could not go anywhere or be with my young grandchildren for fear of the possibility of infecting them or others.

Finally, I looked again at all the health complaints from Northern California. Just searching on the word "rash" I was astonished at how many people had written about their problems with skin rashes that began after the installation of their smart meters.

Additionally during this time, I realized that if I was near people who were transmitting on the new more powerful 3G and 4G phones, I felt like slender sharp needles were going into my ankles, feet, thighs, or mid-back. When within 3 to 4 feet of the smart meters that were installed in my area, the same feeling of needles penetrating my feet and legs would occur. With all these new symptoms, it became obvious they were the result of the new EMF smog that was blanketing our neighborhood and community from the newly installed smart meters, as this was the only thing that was different in my environment. Now that the source of the problem had been identified, it was much easier to find solutions.

My first discovery was that grounding to the earth's energy helps offset electromagnetic radiation, so I started going to the ocean and laying on the sand or the ground for an hour or two each day. Next we brought in a building inspector who helped identify where the EMF exposures were excessive throughout our home and office. Making the changes he recommended and turning the electricity off at night to the back part of our house where we sleep, consistent grounding at the beach, and utilizing energy optimizers—my symptoms gradually lessened.

Today, the combination of minimizing our EMF exposure in our home and office, utilizing a sheet that grounds our bed and a pad that grounds my feet when working on the computer, as well as employing energy optimizers for my body, cell phone, and electronic devices, I am rash free. These lifestyle changes and EMF naturalizing devices allowed me to reenter society and to be able to work again. At 6 months, when I was unable to avoid being around a large crowd of people who are all using their cell phones, my skin still itched for several hours afterwards. When I spent time working in rooms with banks of 50 computers as well as Wi-Fi (e.g., medical library) without adequate antioxidants, I would develop a slight rash on my mouse arm. After 1 year, my lifestyle changes created so much healing, I am happy to share that I now experience no rashes in any of these situations.

Since EMF affects are cumulative and can be delayed (e.g., cancer takes 10 years to show up, itching and headaches can develop hours or days after exposure), it is important to remember that just because we can use grounding pads and energy harmonizing devices to feel more comfortable, it does not mean the harm has been eliminated. The best thing for everyone is to combine as many ways to protect themselves, and eliminate or reduce as much EMF radiation as possible. In this regard it is the same as the hazard of accumulated x-ray radiation, which the medical community always warns to shield against (i.e., lead apron placed on your body for dental X-rays) as well as limit our exposure.

Based on the research I uncovered, every family who has an autistic child, parents with Alzheimer's, or struggling with insomnia and irritability, deserves to be informed that the EMF radiation devices, combined with the thousands of man-made chemicals that were added throughout the 20th century, have led to many changes at the cellular level—changes that result in many physiological and neurological alterations. Neither these chemicals, nor the affects of EMF radiation were tested sufficiently for safety before introducing these toxic biological substances and energies into our world.

Now the list of the ill health effects is continuing to grow as studies on the affects of EMF are being completed—research that should have been conducted before the rapid proliferation of wireless technologies. The list of potential disabling conditions caused by these toxic pollutants include:

Alzheimer's disease
Anorexia
Asthma
Autism
Cancers, including leukemia in children
Blurred vision
Brain fog
Diabetes
Dizziness, vertigo
Decreased immunity
Headaches / migraines
Heart palpitations
Insomnia
Irritability and aggression
MS
Obesity
Ringing in the ears
Skin rashes
Shortness of breath

When I began researching to find help for myself when 12 different health care providers and physicians did not have answers for me, I was horrified and absolutely aghast that there was ample evidence of the harm EMF exposure can cause in the medical literature well before the wireless revolution. Today, the steadily increasing number of studies proving that EMF radiations are not biologically safe should no longer be ignored, the studies prove the future of humanity and life on the planet is at stake.

— Elizabeth Plourde 2013

Preface
3rd Edition

This 3rd edition includes additional studies published since this book's first printing that are proving without doubt the harm to our entire body, and therefore to all of society created by EMF radiation. In this new edition, the truth of how EMF impact life continues to be revealed. The research clearly shows that the symptoms many people feel on exposure to electromagnetic radiation are the result of very real biochemical changes occurring within the cells. The content of this 3rd edition has been rearranged to emphasize how the symptoms are the result of EMF radiation exposure, and not psychosomatic as many studies have tragically implied. Daily, I hear from people wherever utility company smart meters have been installed. They call seeking help for relief of symptoms that have become so debilitating, some have had to leave their jobs, and some even have had to move out of their homes in order to be able to sleep.

We need to listen to these canaries of this new electronic world, as they are showing us that lifestyles need to change and policies need to be implemented to protect our life. We have a social responsibility to guarantee that future generations will not suffer the disabling conditions EMF radiations can create that the scientific studies are continuing to reveal. There are staggering increases in medical care costs. Just the headaches alone that are caused by the radiation have led to many MRIs to rule out brain tumors. Many prescriptions are dispensed to relieve the insomnia, skin rashes, and allergies. Heartbeat irregularities lead some to have pacemakers implanted in their bodies. Thousands of couples are left bereft due to infertility and repeated miscarriages.

Part of the reason that the roll out of EMF radiating devices has been allowed to go on for so long is due to the fact that many articles have been, and continue to be, published that state there is no definitive evidence that EMF radiations create harm to the body. One of the main reasons for this is that studies are not being done in ways that would be capable of revealing harm. Also researchers often interpret the data incorrectly and therefore do not identify harm. I found so many like this that I wanted to include the entire abstract from a researcher who, in 1985, wrote of how incorrect interpretation of data leads to the interpretation that EMF are safe. He wrote in an article titled:

Data Analysis Reveals Significant Microwave-Induced Eye Damage in Humans

"Appleton and McCrossan undertook a study for the U.S. Army at Ft. Monmouth to determine if microwave exposure would cause cataracts. They concluded: 'The comparison showed the groups (microwave exposed vs. not exposed) to be essentially the same and did not support the hypothesis that human cataracts are being caused by chronic exposure to microwaves in the military environment in this country.' There are three major flaws in Appleton and McCrossan's work. First, the exposed group likely included people with little or no exposure. This would tend to minimize the possibility of finding microwave effects. Secondly, their control group consisted of people working with equipment known to cause eye damage. This also would tend to minimize the possibility of finding microwave effects. Thirdly, and most important, they did not do a statistical analysis on their data. When the writer did one, it was found that Appleton and McCrossan have a statistically significant difference between groups, with the microwave exposed showing more lens opacities than would be expected by chance. Thus, their conclusion should have been the opposite of what they stated. It is the uncritical acceptance of negative biological studies of non-ionizing radiation, such as this, that has contributed to the distortion of science in this area of research, and has stimulated public opposition to the installation of such energy sources."[1]

Sadly, even though the above article was written in 1985 with time to stop the avalanching roll out of EMF producing devices, the data published since continues to reveal that microwave radiation can lead to a clouding of the lens and formation of cataracts. This detrimental outcome is described in detail in the section on: EMF – Affect on Blurred Vision.

This is only one biological aspect that has been falsely interpreted. Protecting the brain development of our children has to become a primary objective; many studies reveal damage to every part of the brain, as such our entire societal structure is threatened. The cost to society of hyperactive and autistic children is impossible to calculate since not only are their lives impacted, but also their families, schools, the medical system, and our court systems. All are being stressed and overburdened due to millions being unable to control their behavior. Recognizing that EMF radiation is contributing to the epidemic rise in neurobehavioral problems in children and adults, is not only essential in reducing EMF exposure to slow the rate of the rapidly growing numbers, but also will lead to remedies that will assist them in becoming, and remaining productive members of society. Changes must take place as EMF radiation not only impacts humanity, it is also impacting the lives of all the species that inhabit the earth with us.

— Elizabeth Plourde 2016

EMF Freedom

Solutions for the 21st Century Pollution

3rd Edition

Breaking Away from the

MASS CONSciousness Series:

Insights Beyond Tunnel Vision

Introduction

In 2009, we became aware that utility companies were installing electrical smart meters in Northern California. Smart meters utilize EMF (electromagnetic fields) to wirelessly transmit customers' energy use back to the utility company. EMF frequencies are classified as non-ionizing radiation. They have been thought to be safe compared to the ionizing radiations that emanate from X-rays, nuclear power plants, and atomic bombs. However, researchers are revealing non-ionizing radiations are biological hazards also.

Having been a health consultant for over 15 years, I began hearing the health complaints from people in Northern California of migraines, insomnia, heart palpitations, and shortness of breath. In 2011 after they began to install electric smart meters in Southern California, the same pattern of symptoms emerged: migraines, insomnia, heart palpitations, shortness of breath, as well as itching skin and rashes.

It is clear that neither biochemists nor human physiologists could have been involved in the decisions to go ahead and smart meter grid entire states like California, or entire nations, or the entire modern world. It makes absolutely no sense to employ these technologies that are radiating electromagnetic radiation 24 hours a day with no relief, and leaving nowhere for people to go to escape them.

Yes, the studies to date have been conflicting, because it is difficult to measure what you cannot see with the naked eye. This too was the situation for Dr. Ignaz Semmelweis in the 1840s who identified that doctors going from autopsy to assisting in childbirth were responsible for the 20% of the women who were continually dying from child bed fever (puerperal infection). He arranged an experiment of washing hands between autopsy and assisting with childbirths. That simple act reduced the outrageously high number of mothers dying down to only 1%. But, because the bacteria could not be seen, doctors refused to believe they were infecting their patients and kept on killing 20% of our women for an additional 30 years before washing of hands was adopted as an essential, common sense answer that is necessary to save lives. Dr. Semmelweis died in a mental institution before being able to see his life-saving research become accepted as common sense.

Today, the world is in the same place regarding EMF radiations that cannot be seen. Without the proper studies being conducted subjecting laboratory animals to EMF exposure for 24 hours a day (as the smart meters do) for at least 10 years, so that long term effects can be either identified or ruled out, the plans to smart meter grid the world is pure folly, with wide ranging and possibly irreversible repercussions.

Non-ionizing and Ionizing Radiation Clarified

The energy from non-ionizing radiation (cell phones and wireless devices), which has been considered as safe in the past, is enough to vibrate molecules, compared to ionizing radiation that has enough energy to alter the chemical bonds that hold molecules together. Ionizing radiation (x-rays) is cumulative and causes the most damage in rapidly dividing cells as identified by the fact that the cells of the bone marrow, reproductive organs, lining of the intestine, and the skin suffer the most damage from exposure. The studies in this book highlight that these same areas—reproductive organs, intestinal lining, and skin— experience damage as well when exposed to the non-ionizing EMF radiation. The affects are cumulative, as they too buildup over time, it just takes longer for the results to manifest into disabling symptoms and diseases.

Studies are beginning to accumulate that identify EMF exposures are NOT harmless, and that they are impacting all life on every level. Our biochemistry is so complex (cell shape is just one of the 100s of variable factors), and each person is subjected to such varying degrees of radiation and absorption, it is impossible to even imagine the entirety of the impact not only on this generation, but on generations to come. There are biochemical explanations for the symptoms people are experiencing due to the fact the EMF exposure alters cell membrane permeability, changes the shape of our red blood cells, and vibrates our entire DNA. These changes are difficult to detect and are causing great expense to be incurred by our society and medical systems as expensive medical workups are being done—finding no medical reasons for the symptoms of headaches or heart palpitations. In addition, studies have identified that EMF impact fertility, leading to irreversible infertility in lab animals. Years of daily, continuous exposure could lead to total infertility for the human race. This is because EMF radiation have been found to:

Vibrate our DNA.
Increase DNA breaks and rearrangements in sperm and
    testicle cells.
Increase cell death in the testicles.
Create DNA breaks in the embryos in mice.

It is important to address that there are many researchers and committees who are recognizing these health threats, yet their warnings do not appear to be heeded. In May 2011, the Council of Europe summarized their findings in their report on *The Potential Dangers of Electromagnetic Fields and Their Effect on the Environment* stating:

"The potential health effects of the very low frequency of electromagnetic fields surrounding power lines and electrical devices are the subject of ongoing research and a significant amount of public debate. While electrical and electromagnetic fields in certain frequency bands have fully beneficial effects which are applied in medicine, other non-ionizing frequencies, be they sourced from extremely low frequencies, power lines or certain high frequency waves used in the fields of radar, telecommunications and mobile telephony, appear to have more or less potentially harmful, non-thermal, biological effects on plants, insects and animals, as well as the human body when exposed to levels that are below the official threshold values."

"One must respect the precautionary principle and revise the current threshold values; waiting for high levels of scientific and clinical proof can lead to very high health and economic costs, as was the case in the past with asbestos, leaded petrol and tobacco."

"After analyzing the scientific studies available to date, and also following the hearings for expert opinions organized in the context of the Committee on the Environment, Agriculture and Local and Regional Affairs, there is sufficient evidence of potentially harmful effects of electromagnetic fields on fauna, flora and human health to react and to guard against potentially serious environmental and health hazards."[2]

This committee recognized the health hazards of EMF in 2011, yet wireless technologies have continued to proliferate throughout the world, and throughout 2015 utility smart meters continued to be rapidly installed across the United States.

This book is a compilation of some of the many studies that have been published to date that document the numerous harmful effects of EMF radiation. Please read the titles in the References section, as the titles of the studies alone tell the story of the huge disabling health impact EMF radiations are creating every day.

Throughout the book the terms EMF and EMR are used. EMF stands for *electromagnetic fields*, EMR stands for *electromagnetic radiation*. The electromagnetic fields put out radiation so these terms are interchangeable, and have essentially the same meaning. RF is also used and means *radio frequency*, while ELF means *extremely low frequency* (i.e., household current),.

Some of the material that is presented in this book may be a little technical and difficult to understand. Our biochemistry at the level of the cell is so complex, researchers still do not fully understand how it all works. In all my years of research, I cannot tell you the number of studies that end with "we do not know" and suggest further research should be conducted to answer the questions that are still unresolved.

We believe that by looking at all the information provided as pieces of a jigsaw puzzle, which eventually reveals more and more of the complete picture, that by the end of the book all the pieces will fall into their rightful places and you will have a clearer picture of this health challenge in this 21st century.

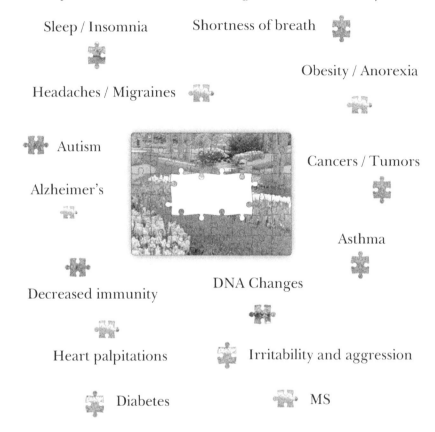

Sleep / Insomnia   Shortness of breath

Obesity / Anorexia

Headaches / Migraines

Autism

Cancers / Tumors

Alzheimer's

Asthma

Decreased immunity   DNA Changes

Heart palpitations   Irritability and aggression

Diabetes   MS

As the 20th and 21st Century Collide

In the 20th century thousands of man-made chemicals were introduced into our environment, many of which are toxic. Now in the 21st century excessive EMF radiations are bombarding our already chemically burdened bodies. Unfortunately, these two assaults have the makings of the *perfect storm* that is challenging our bodies' defense systems.

Excessive chemical and electromagnetic radiation burdens have resulted in many developing symptoms of multiple chemical sensitivities (MCS) and electromagnetic sensitivity (EMS), also

known as electromagnetic hypersensitivity (EHS). Individual differences in toxic chemical loads are one reason some experience
EHS symptoms while others do not. The studies show EMF exposure opens the barriers of the brain, gut, and placenta, which
are designed to protect the vulnerable areas of the body and developing fetus from toxic chemicals and pathogens. People who
are already on toxic overload are being additionally burdened
by EMF radiations that are further altering their biochemistry,
resulting in their experiencing a wide variety of symptoms that
are new to our generation.

Our medical systems have not caught up to these changes
and many health care providers are not trained to recognize or
treat these chemically and electrosensitive people. Many go from
doctor to doctor without answers. Hopefully, if you or someone
in your family is being affected, the information provided in this
book will assist you in finding and receiving the help you need.

After you have read this book:

1. You will have the awareness that EMF radiations, by
    altering the electrical charge of every cell in our bodies,
    disrupt the vast complex of our cells' chemical reactions.

2. You will be armed with the knowledge and actions nec-
    essary to protect yourself and your family from this 21st
    century assault.

Part 1

EMF – General Background

Chapter 1

Electromagnetic Frequencies

The top of the Electromagnetic Frequency Spectrum chart on the following page separates the frequencies between non-ionizing and ionizing radiation. The chart further divides the spectrum into the types of rays: microwaves, infrared, visible, ultraviolet, x-rays, and gamma rays.

The remainder of the chart is a blowup of the 1 Hz (hertz) to 100 GHz (gigahertz) frequencies, because these are the radiations that we are being increasingly exposed to and therefore are discussed throughout this book. The chart shows the frequency ranges for many of the electronic devices utilized today. These include:

- Radio and television transmissions
- Cell phones
- Smart meters (electric, gas, and water utilities)
- Microwave ovens
- Wi-Fi (which now ranges up to 60 and 80 GHz)
- Radar

Even though the number of frequencies and the extent of the ranges have been gradually increasing to add bandwidth availability for the millions of utility smart meters, Wi-Fi, and cell phones that are continually being added every year, very few long-term studies have been conducted in these frequency ranges to determine the extent and breath of their impact on humans.

The Electromagnetic Frequency Spectrum

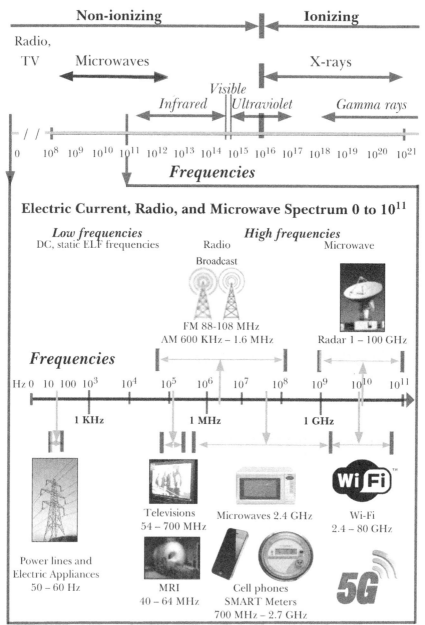

Figure 1. Electromagnetic device frequencies.

Legend: Hz (hertz), KHz (kilohertz, 10^3 Hz), MHz (megahertz, 10^6 Hz), GHz (gigahertz, 10^9 Hz)

EMF – Wireless Devices and Frequencies

Cell Phones
700 MHz – 2.7 GHz

Bluetooth
2.4 – 5 GHz

Cordless Phones
900 MHz / 2.4 – 5.8 GHz

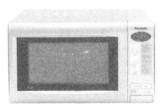

Microwave Oven
2.4 GHz

Computers / Laptops / Tablets
2.4 GHz (with built-in Wi-Fi)

Wi-Fi
2.4, 5.8, 60 and 80 GHz

Cell Phone Frequencies

The cell or mobile phone frequency of Global System for Mobile Communication (GSM) replaced the earlier analog or 1G (1st generation) phones. This GSM, also termed as 2G or 2nd generation, utilizes the ranges of 850 – 1900 MHz in the Americas and 900 – 1800 MHz for the rest of the world.

GSM was followed by the Universal Mobile Telecommunications Systems (UMTS) or 3G (3rd generation), which utilizes 850 – 1700, 1885 – 2025 MHz and 2110 – 2200 MHz.

Global Cellular Frequencies

	Generation	Hz	MHz
North America	2G and 3G	800	1900
	4G	700/800	1700 – 2100
	4G		2500 – 2700
Europe	4G	800	1800 & 2600

Sources: Antennas website. Cellular antennas, amplifiers and repeaters are frequency specific. Retrieved March 20, 2013 from: www.wpsantennas.com/cellular-frequency-information.aspx

CodeNice website: AT&T T-Mobile 2G 3G 4G LTE Frequencies. Retrieved August 13, 2015 from: http://codenice.com/att-t-mobile-2g-3g-4g-lte-frequencies/

WorldTimeZone website. Retrieved June 6, 2015 from: www.worldtimezone.com/gsm.html

As a result of all these overlapping systems, everyone is exposed to a greater number of MHz frequency ranges. Since everyone carries a mobile cell phone, each with different service providers, everyone is subjected to the following multiple frequency bands—most of the time:

Cell Phone Frequencies – 2G, 3G, 4G

700 Hz
800 Hz
850 Hz
900 Hz
1700 – 2100 MHz (1.7 – 2.1 GHz)
2500 – 2700 MHz (2.5 – 2.7 GHz)

Each cell phone provider has its own antennas on the cell towers, which adds to the radiation load. It is difficult to understand why there is so little regard for health when a 2008 study identified that to their knowledge they were the first to study long-term exposure (1 year) to the new 3G (GSM) phones and their affect on memory, even though they were introduced in 2001 and then mass marketed to the public by the mid-2000s, with the public responding in great numbers—well before research studies were performed to determine their safety—well before the first investigation into the long-term effects on memory.[3]

Yet, even though studies have now identified 3G phones harm memory, so little attention has been paid to the evidence of the great biological harm this portends (e.g., Alzheimer's in adults, digital dementia in children) that, as of February 2013, the number of cell phones in use around the world climbed to close to 7 billion. China is ranked as having the most, followed by India, while the U.S. ranked 3rd in the world with over 328 million registered users (June 2011).[4]

Cell phones, since they update their location on a regular basis, are periodically emitting *pulsing* radiation even when they are not being used. As such, people are exposed to EMF radiation from their cell phones while they are on standby mode. In public places there is so much radiation due to the vast number of cell phones (as well as wireless technologies in use), researchers find it is impossible to measure, without isolating the individual, the radiation each is exposed to from their own phone during a cell phone's updating cycle.[5]

The FCC (Federal Communications Commission) requires that all devices sold in the U.S. meet a minimum guideline for safe human exposure to radio frequency energy. The unit they use is a SAR or specific absorption rate, which is a measure of the rate that RF (radio frequency) energy is absorbed by the body when using a mobile phone. "The SAR is a value that corresponds to the relative amount of RF energy absorbed in the head of a user of a wireless handset." It is a measure for the thermal or heat effect of the RF radiation.[6] Its unit is W/kg or watts per kilogram. The SAR of 1.6 W/kg is the maximum allowed in the United States for safety, yet as you will see in the studies presented throughout this book, biological harm occurs

at levels that are well below 1.6 W/kg. Indeed this identification
of harm is validated by researchers from Greece, Sweden and the
U.S. In looking at the interaction between man-made EMF and
the energy transfer within a cell they found:

1. "The energy absorbed by living matter during exposure
    to environmentally accounted EMFs is normally well
    below the thermal level."
2. "All existing methods for *SAR* estimation, especially those
    based upon tissue conductivity and internal electric field,
    have serious deficiencies."
3. "The only method to estimate *SAR* without large error
    is by measuring temperature increases within biological
    tissue, which normally are negligible for environmental
    EMF intensities, and thus cannot be measured."

Based on their findings, the whole idea of this maximum value of SAR that is allowed by the U.S. FCC, and other government
regulators around the world may be generating an entirely false
sense of safety. This is so different from what we have been told
that I am including these researchers entire conclusion:

"*SAR* actually refers to thermal [heat] effects, while the vast
majority of the recorded biological effects from man-made
non-ionizing environmental radiation are non-thermal.
Even if *SAR* could be accurately estimated for a whole tissue,
organ, or body, the biological/health effect is determined by
tiny amounts of energy/power absorbed by specific biomol-
ecules, which cannot be calculated. Moreover, it depends
upon field parameters not taken into account in *SAR* calcula-
tion. Thus, *SAR* should not be used as the primary dosimetric quantity [measuring the amount of radiation absorbed],
but used only as a complementary measure, always reporting
the estimating method and the corresponding error. Radia-
tion/field intensity along with additional physical parameters
(such as frequency, modulation etc), which can be directly
and more accurately measured on the surface of biological
tissues, should constitute the primary measure for EMF exposures, in spite of similar uncertainty to predict the biological effect due to non-linearity."[7]

Dr. Martin Pall, a researcher and biochemistry professor, has published several papers that are in alignment with these conclusions. He states that the action of EMF microwave radiation is on activation of the cells' voltage-gated calcium channels (VGCC) [cell membrane openings specific for calcium]. The biological importance of these is discussed in the Section on EMF – Affect on Calcium Balance. He cites the many cellular changes that are seen that corroborate this type of effect. Cells with high numbers of VGCC are found in the nervous system, heart and testicles, which all show alterations when exposed to EMF. VGCC activation triggers neurotransmitter and hormone release, leading to diverse neuropsychiatric effects. VGCC activated by EMF can explain many of the symptoms and diseases that are being seen today and identified throughout this book. With this type of effect, Dr. Pall has also concluded that making safety guidelines based on thermal effects is not valid, even stating it is "indefensible," and calls for a shift towards safety standards that recognize EMF activates VGCC is essential—a paradigm shift that must take place.[8]

These researchers reveal that the FCC's use of SAR to prove whether harm could occur is meaningless, as it does not measure how EMF radiations harm our cells Sadly, by looking at the wrong measurement and giving the public a false sense of safety, millions have adopted 24 hour a day ubiquitous use of EMF devices, potentially creating long-term cellular harm.

Wi-Fi Networks and Wireless — A Mini Cell Tower

Today almost all public buildings, including hotels, vacation rentals, restaurants, and coffee shops boast they have Wi-Fi available for their customers. They have installed it to attract more business, but it leaves few places where people can go to be free of EMF radiation. Anytime there a Wi-Fi router, or device with Wi-Fi capacity in a room or near you, it is like having a mini cell tower next to you—constantly. It functions the same as tower, but may not have the power levels emitted from tower configuration with 1,000s of signals. It is still worth considering it harmful.

There are communities like Mountain View, California where free coverage by a citywide Wi-Fi system has been offered. Forbes magazine reported there are rumors that private companies want to make free Wi-Fi available everywhere.[9]

EMF FREEDOM

Smart Meter Installations: Electric, Gas, and Water

Wireless electrical smart meters are part of the new electrical grid that is being rapidly deployed around the United States and around the world. It consists of a wireless network of connections that make it possible for utility companies to determine a customer's usage without physically sending employees out to read meters for billing purposes. They have adopted this program stating it will result in more efficient use of energy resources. Smart meters are being implemented for natural gas and water as well.

Electric Digital Smart Meter

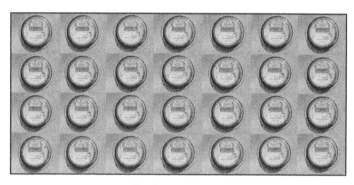

Bank of Smart Meters
[business locations, apartment or condo complexs]

Common smart meter frequencies utilized by utility companies:
  Electrical   = 900 MHz and 2.4 GHz (2400 MHz)*
  Water = 900 MHz and 2.4 GHz (2400 MHz)*
  Gas = 450 – 470 MHz and 800 MHz / 1.9 GHz (1900 MHz).[10]

* The 2.4 GHz (2400 MHz) is the same frequency microwave ovens use to cook food.

Harmful Health Effects

The smart meters are active 24 hours, 7 days a week, 365 days a year. Collectively they add to the massive amounts of electromagnetic smog created by television, radio, Wi-Fi, cell phone and cordless phone frequencies that are already bombarding and microwaving us. In addition to the frequencies smart meters emit, they have had to boost the cell towers' power capacities to be able to read the meters. The meters are designed to transmit to a collector or web meter, which has an extra antenna that transmits the energy usage to the utility company one or two times per day. To create this report each meter sends out micro blasts multiple times a minute. This *pulse* type of radiation is much more harmful to our cells than continuous steady radiation exposure.

This additional electromagnetic smog is causing health problems for people who are electromagnetically sensitive or health challenged. Since all radiations have cumulative effects, the numbers of those affected will continually grow and many more will eventually develop electromagnetic hypersensitivity (EHS) symptoms. A survey conducted in 2013 found that many more individuals reported new or increased symptoms after smart meters were installed on their residences.[11]

Do you or someone in your family have new unexplained health issues or an increase in symptoms? Does it coincide with the installation of smart meters in your neighborhood? There is a massive amount of information regarding the whole constellation of symptoms people have been experiencing since the start of smart meter installations. The studies in this book explain the biochemical reasons for their symptoms.

Another point that needs to be brought up is that many appliances on the market today already have built-in computers and wireless devices. The goal is for all appliances to eventually communicate with your home's smart meter on an ongoing basis. The downside is that more wireless radiations will be operating within your living space, adding to the already excessive EMF exposure penetrating your residence. Some people have had to return their new appliances. Once they were brought into their home, they developed electromagnetic symptoms and stayed sick until the offending appliance was removed from their home.

The millions of people who occupy buildings and residences that now have EMF emitting smart utility meters should be concerned. A study that investigated the effects of the *pulsed* radio frequency 900 MHz (used in cell phones and some smart meters) on nerve cells of the brains of birds, found that 76% of the brain cells increased their rates of firing, while other cells had decreased rates of activity. Seeing such changes, these researchers concluded that *pulsing* cell phone use has the potential to impact human brains.[12] Since some smart meters *pulse* the same 900 MHz frequency, they become suspect of this same effect on humans.

Responding to a questionnaire, people living less than 300 meters (984 feet) from a cell phone base station antenna reported statistically significant symptoms of nausea, headache, dizziness, irritability, discomfort, nervousness, depression, sleep disturbance, memory loss and lowering of libido (sex drive) compared to those living greater than 300 meters (984 feet) from an antenna. The results led the researchers to suggest that cell tower base station antennas should not be located any closer than 300 meters (984 feet) to people to minimize exposure, and lessen probability of producing symptoms.[13]

The United States NASA (National Aeronautics and Space Administration) recognizes the hazardousness of microwave radiation (which is now surrounding us through the utility companies' smart meters). Aware of the harm it can cause led to their creation of a safety training manual for *RF & Microwave Radiation Hazard Awareness*, which presents the Safety and Mission Assurance Code 803.2. In the course they state:

Radiation is energy transmitted through space in the form of electromagnetic waves or subatomic particles.

- Examples include:
  - — Radio frequency (RF) radiation, microwaves
  - — Infrared, visible, ultraviolet light
  - — X-rays and gamma rays.

They cite a U.S. OSHA (Occupational Safety & Health Administration) reference code that states:

- OSHA 29 CFR 1910.97 (a)(2)(i)
  — For normal environmental conditions and for incident electromagnetic energy of frequencies from 10 MHz to 100 GHz, the radiation protection guide is 10 mW/cm2* (milliwatts per square centimeter) as averaged over any possible 0.1 hour period (6 minute period).

    * The density of radiation hitting a surface area.

- Observed thermal effects in areas exceeding the MPE (Maximum Permissible Exposure Safety Limit):
  — Heating of the body (developing fetus is at no greater risk than mother)
  — Cataracts
  — Reduced sperm count in males
  — Perception
  — Auditory (>100 mW/cm2) buzzing, clicking, hissing
  — Work disturbance (based on animal studies).

- RF current effects:
  — Shocks or burns
  — Neural stimulation (extremely low frequency = 0 – 3 kHz) (tissue damage at 10 x MPE).

- Signs and symptoms of possible over exposure may include:
  — Confusion
  — Vertigo
  — Headache
  — Blurred vision
  — Overall nauseous feeling
  — Body heating (heat stress)
  — Shocks and burns
  — Bad or metallic taste in mouth.

- RF radiation.
  Most documented harmful effects associated with RF are due to hyperthermia (increased body temperature):
  — The eyes and testicles are of primary concern due to their inability to dissipate heat.
  — The lens of the eye is vulnerable to heating and can lead to cataracts (clouding of the lens).
  — Testicular function is strongly influenced by temperature and an increase in temperature decreases sperm cell survival.[14]

This course developed by the government shows it recognizes electromagnetic radiation can cause harm and those exposed to it need to be educated on how to protect themselves from its possible damaging effects. The list of symptoms from this course should make utility companies that are installing the new microwave transmitting smart meters take notice that their meters are making people sick due to the electromagnetic radiations the meters emit. Most of these symptoms are what people are reporting after their microwave emitting smart meters are installed on their residences and in their neighborhoods.

Chapter 2

General Background

In a 1991 study, researchers made the statement that:

"There is currently no definitive evidence of an association between exposure to EMF and the alleged risks."

Yet, at the same time these researchers identified the very real problem of science attempting to prove the effects of what cannot be seen with the eyes. They also stated that:

"Due to problems and limitations inherent in future studies (misconceptions about exposure levels, uncertainty about field variability, criticisms of surrogate measures), this question is unlikely to ever be answered with certainty."[15]

The problem: investigators have been attempting to design studies to detect changes in biological tissues that are being caused by something they cannot see. Compound this with the unlimited number of variables that can impact any study, it is very difficult to design and implement studies that produce definitive answers. This is why there are so many conflicting results reported in the available literature.

In 1998, evidence of damage to DNA in breakage of its vital strands, abnormal cell division, and cell death by EMF was clearly demonstrated. The researchers found that the ability to damage the DNA depends upon cell shape, size, and orientation, and whether unstable molecules (free radicals) are formed by the exposure. Each of these variables created a different outcome.

The reasons for conflicting conclusions and no evidence of damage reported by some studies are that it not only depends upon the shape and size of the cell, it is also dependent on the direction of the EMF, whether the radiation is vertically or horizontally applied. Exposing human amniotic fluid (the fluid that surrounds the fetus during development) cells to vertically generated 50 Hz (standard household current in U.S.) EMF creates no DNA damage, whereas horizontally applied EMF creates DNA damage that shows up as abnormal cell division.[16]

A study published in *Electromagnetic Biology and Medicine* identified that conflicting outcomes from the studies can arise from differences in temperature, background radiation, and the amount of light. Different laboratory settings would have differences in each of these variables, which could lead to conflicting results arising from the studies. Recognition of this led these researchers to state the impact of the many variables in laboratory conditions are often not given adequate consideration.[17]

By 2004, an investigator stated that other chemicals involved in cellular processes may increase the ability of EMF to damage DNA. The combination could lead to genetic instability and disturbances in cell division.[18] Since we all have slightly different chemical make ups, it is difficult to control these types of variables.

In 2006 and 2008, the U.S. Environmental Protection Agency (EPA) published reports recommending ways to improve children's health risk assessments, such as looking at time of exposure to outcome.[19] This does identify the U.S. government's concern over children being put at risk. However, actions to decrease the amount of EMF exposure are not being taken. This is in the face of an ever increasing number of studies that now cast sufficient doubt on the safety of wireless technologies and smart meters. These published studies make the case for immediate removal of wireless technologies as rapidly as possible, and the cessation of any more smart meter installations, as well as their replacement with the old analog meters that have been safe for us over the last 100 years.

Dr. Stephen Genuis in a 2008 study identifying the harm EMF are causing in study after study stated:

"... epidemiological analyses continue to suggest considerable potential for injury and affliction as a result of NIR (non-ionizing radiation) [EMF] exposure. As environmental health has not been emphasized in medical education, some clinicians are not fully aware of possible EMF-related health problems and, as a result, manifestations of a-NIR [adverse non-ionizing radiation] may remain misdiagnosed and ineffectually managed. It is important for physicians and public health officials to be aware of the fundamental science and clinical implications of EMF exposure."[20]

In 2009 a panel of scientists met in Norway to discuss the:

". . . existing scientific evidence and public health implications of the unprecedented global exposures to artificial electromagnetic fields (EMF). EMF exposures (static to 300 GHz) result from the use of electric power and from wireless telecommunications technologies for voice and data transmission, energy, security, military and radar use in weather and transportation. The Scientific Panel recognizes that the body of evidence on EMF requires a new approach to protection of public health; the growth and development of the fetus, and of children; and argues for strong preventative actions. New, biologically-based public exposure standards are urgently needed to protect public health worldwide."[21]

In 2010, one of the researchers on the panel, Dr. Johansson, along with Dr. Dämvik expressed more warnings that the current accepted levels of exposure limits, which have been deemed to be safe, are far above what are beginning to be identified as safe limits. They concluded:

"A thorough examination of the state of research shows many serious indications of possible health risks from exposure very far below existing limits for EMF. Case law, for other types of exposure, also shows that the precautionary principle can be applied on the basis of weaker evidence than that. Our investigation shows that the precautionary principle is not being used for its intended purpose in relation to exposure to EMF. The reason for this position is that decision-makers are being misled by inaccurate risk assessments."[22]

These researchers are warning us that without complete documentation of safety it is better to proceed with caution, embracing the *precautionary principle*. Yet this is not being implemented for wireless technologies.

A 2011 study identified that longitudinal studies involving more than a few days or weeks, as well as studies on children and adolescents are scarce. Expressing their concerns over the lack of sufficient research, they warned:

> "Nevertheless, the rapid technological development and anticipated increase in exposure levels warrant the conduct of further longitudinal studies. Due to the widespread use of wireless communication technologies potential adverse health effects would have major public health consequences."[23]

Major harm to all life on the planet is revealed by a study published in 2013, which reviewed 113 studies that investigated ecological effects of EMF in the range of 10 MHz to 3.6 GHz (3600 MHz). Of those reviewed, 65% of the studies found EMF created alterations at both high as well as at low dosages. Of these, 50% revealed effects on animals, and 75% showed effects on plants. These effects were found to be greater:

- With longer durations of EMF exposure,
- When utilizing GSM (Global System for Mobile Communication cell phone service).[24]

Today, there are enough studies that identify the harm created by EMF radiation that the rapid deployment of wireless technologies needs to be reconsidered. Technological development should include safeguards that protect our health today and for future generations.

Chapter 3

Increasing Incidences in Diseases

Organizations around the world are concerned about the rapidly increasing incidences of several debilitating and costly diseases. They are attempting to discover why they are increasing—some at alarming rates. This book presents the evidence that EMF radiation could be a major contributing factor behind their fast rising numbers.

Alzheimer's Disease – Worldwide

According to the 2015 World Alzheimer's Report cases are briskly rising:
- 48.6 million
  Projected to double every 20 years to:
    74.7 million by 2030
    115.4 million by 2050
- Annual cost today is $818 billion

  Authorities cite economic globalization and development in developing countries as reasons for the increase.[25] This theory goes along with the fact that microwave technologies accompany the modern services brought to developing countries. This may improve their ability to communicate with the rest of the world, but at what cost?

Alzheimer's Disease – America
- 5.3 million with Alzheimer's – 63% are women
- 6th leading cause of death – 1 out of every 3 seniors
- $226 billion in annual costs
- Every 67 seconds someone develops Alzheimer's
  By 2050, the rate will increase to 1 every 33 seconds, with costs estimated to rise to $1.1 trillion[26]

Autoimmune Disorders – Worldwide
Worldwide rate increase:
- Type 1 diabetes increasing 3% per year since 1950
- MS rates doubled in females from 1980 to 1990
- Lupus mortality rates doubled from 1979 to 1998[27]

Autoimmune Disorders – America
The prevalence is estimated to be 23.5 million – 75% are women:
- Occurrence has doubled in 30 years
- Prevalence greater than the 9 million with cancer
- Almost equal to the 22 million with heart disease
- 5th to 7th leading cause of death in females (depending on age)[28]

Asthma – America
- 9 million children – leading to chronic childhood illness
- Chemicals are part of the problem
  9/11 World Trade Center intense dust clouds from collapse: 13.5% of those exposed now have asthma, compared to 8.4% who had no exposure[29]

Diabetes – Worldwide
The rates are rising much faster than projected.

	Prevalence (estimated) 2000[30]	Projected for 2030[30]	Actual reported in 2013[31]
Population	2.8%	4.4%	8.3%
Incidence (millions)	171	366	382

The 2013 incidence rate by far exceeded the 2030 projections.

Diabetes – America
The numbers in America are also rising rapidly.

Diabetes in America

	2007[32]	2013[33]
Population	8.0%	9.3%
Diagnosed (millions)	17.9	21.0
Undiagnosed (millions)	5.7	8.1
Pre diabetes (millions)	57.0	86.0
New cases per year (millions)	1.6	1.7

These dramatic changes occurred in just 5 years.

Obesity – America
In the United States, the percentage of the population classified as obese has grown dramatically since the 1970s, when cell
phones and sunscreens* were introduced.

Obesity Percentages in America[34]

Age groups	1970s	2010
6 – 11 year olds	4.0%	18.8%
12 – 19 year olds	6.0%	18.1%
Adults (20 and older)	13 – 17%	36.0%

* See *Sunscreens – Biohazard: Treat As Hazardous Waste*, by E. Plourde. New Voice
  Publications; Irvine, CA; 2011).

Strokes – England
The Stroke Association in England identified the rise in strokes
in younger men aged 40 – 54.
  • 2000 = 4,260 hospital admissions
  • 2014 = 6,221 hospital admissions[35]

Strokes – America
United States study identified that strokes under age 55 increased
in a little over 10 years:
  • 1993 – 1994 = 12.9%
  • 2005   = 18.6%[36]

Autism – America

In 1970 autism was termed *childhood schizophrenia*.
The incidence rate in 1970 was 1 in 2,222.[37]

	All ages **2009**	Age 8 **2010**	Age 8 **2018**[37]
Boys	1 in 58	1 in 42	1 in 27
Girls		1 in 189	1 in 116
Boys and girls	1 in 100	1 in 68	1 in 44
Ratio boys to girls	4 to 1		4 to 1

England, Japan, Sweden, Canada all have similar rates that have risen just as dramatically.

Dr. Stephanie Seneff, senior research scientist at the MIT Computer Science and Artificial Intelligence Laboratory (CSAIL), has reviewed the incidence rate and statistical trend of autism. She states, if the current trend continues unchecked, her calculations show us:

By 2032, every other child born in America will be autistic.[38]

Bipolar Disorder Diagnosis – America

Hospital admissions have increased dramatically:

Bipolar Disorder Diagnosis in America[39]

(per 100,000)

	1994 - 1995	2002 - 2003
Youth visits (0 – 19 years old)	25	1,003
Adults visits (20 and over)	905	1,679

As wireless devices have proliferated by the billions during these years of rapidly increasing incidence rates in these diseases, wireless in our workplaces and in our homes needs to be considered and recognized as part of the reason behind these dramatic increases. This book details how the body is being biochemically impacted by EMF that result in many changes such as these in our overall health.

Chapter 4

EMF – Compromise the Body's Protective Barriers

EMF – Compromise Cell Membranes
All cells in the body are enclosed by a protective membrane.

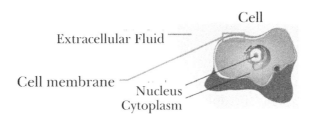

EMF radiations have the ability to alter our cells outer protective membrane's normal electrical potential. This potential is created by the difference in the electrical charge between the inside and the outside of the cell. The charge is part of a gate keeping system cells use to *allow* in what they need, *keep in* what is required to perform their functions, and *allow out* what must be discharged. This is crucial as the integrity of the membranes' charge must be maintained to protect cells and assure their normal functioning.

Warning

Potential Health Effects – compromised membrane integrity:

> The effects are too numerable to estimate as
> every cellular reaction is placed in jeopardy,
> therefore any disabling outcome could occur

EMF – Affect on Calcium Balance
One of the primary ways that cells maintain the narrow electrical potential (field) across their membranes is through a calcium gate within the cell membrane that is regulated by voltage,

the VGCC discussed in Chapter 1. Studies are identifying that EMF radiation activates this calcium gate in the cell membrane and leads to an abnormal increase in the concentration of calcium inside the cell.[40] Calcium is involved in a multitude of essential tasks throughout the body, and it can only perform its functions correctly when its concentration is maintained in a very narrow range both inside and outside of each cell.

When the normal balance of calcium is altered, its many life preserving functions are endangered. Calcium is required for enzymatic reactions, proper glucose metabolism, and for the ability of the muscles to contract. In addition, calcium is also required for proper life supporting cell-to-cell communication, providing the opportunity for nerve cells to respond and react to a stimulus.[41]

Additionally, in 2012, researchers identified radio frequency exposure changes the ability of calcium to act as a buffer in the brains of mice, which would result in cell death. They stated their findings confirm radio frequency exposure has the possibility of creating brain injury.[42]

The main point to remember is that the functions of calcium in the body are numerous and complex with a very narrow concentration that must be maintained for proper functioning. Its delicate balance is disrupted by EMF exposure—a disruption that can create a multitude of health issues.

Warning

Potential Health Effects – loss of calcium balance disrupts many bodily activities including:

Blood pressure
Blood clotting
Bone metabolism
Sugar metabolism
Brain cell loss

EMF – Affect on Antioxidant Balance

The body's daily biochemical reactions involve a process called oxidation and reduction.

Oxidation is essential and is the result of the chemical interactions that occur with oxygen. When these reactions produce molecules that contain both oxygen and an extra electron, they are known as reactive oxygen species (ROS). ROS are essential for many reactions in the body. However, they are very powerful and need to be kept in balance with antioxidants.

Free radicals are molecules with extra electrons but no oxygen. Antioxidants contribute electrons that can then combine with the unpaired electrons of the free radicals or ROS and neutralize the harmful effects caused by the free electrons.

When in excess, both free radicals and ROS have the ability to cause harmful cellular changes if they are not neutralized by antioxidants. This is why there has been so much health advice to include an abundant supply of antioxidants in our diets.

Studies on rat brains have identified that EMF exposure not only generates ROS, it acts as a stressor on the systems that are designed to control the brain's oxidative balance.[43] The resultant "oxidative stress" and increase in the number of ROS may be too great to be balanced by the brain's normal supply of antioxidants, which could result in brain cell damage.

Warning

Potential Health Effects – increased free radicals and ROS damaging brain cells:

Any condition regarding brain functioning including cognitive functioning, memory, aging, and cancer.

In investigating the ability of EMF radiation to increase free radicals, they found that EMF radiation would lead to a lifetime of persistently elevated free radical concentrations, resulting in a continuing increase in DNA damage. One consequence would be the inhibition of the effects of melatonin (see EMF – Affect on Sleep / Insomnia). Based on these findings, the researchers concluded:

> "Taken together, these EMF induced reactions could lead to a higher incidence of DNA damage and therefore, to an increased risk of tumor development."[44]

One of these researchers in a different article identified that EMF stimulate white blood cells to release free radicals. Additionally, the chronic stimulation of the white blood cells causes actions that increase ROS that damage DNA, which in turn can lead to more free radicals. This led him to conclude that these actions have the ability to lead to the development of cancer.[45]

Finding similar results, laboratory rats exposed for 2 hours a day for 35 days to a 2.45 GHz (2450 MHz) frequency showing DNA damage and increased oxidation led the researchers to warn:

> "The study concludes that the chronic exposure to these radiations may cause significant damage to the brain, which may be an indication of possible tumor promotion . . ."[46]

Warning
Potential Health Effects – increased free radicals and ROS leading to DNA damage:
Cancer

In investigating the possibility of damage from cell phone radiation, researchers exposed rats to 900 MHz at SAR 1.08 W/kg for 1 hour a day for 3 weeks. They found a significant increase in brain oxidative stress after the exposure. They also determined that giving the rats garlic powder (a powerful antioxidant) has a protective effect against this oxidative stress.[47]

These same researchers exposed rats to 1.8 GHz at SAR 0.4 W/kg for 1 hour a day for 3 weeks and found that it, too, creates oxidation in brain tissue, which was also reduced with garlic.[48]

When researchers exposed rats to 900 MHz mobile phone radiation for 2 hours a day for 45 days, they identified the rats showed significant changes in antioxidant enzymes. Since this indicates the radiation created an overproduction of reactive oxygen species (ROS) that can damage cells, they concluded:

"Our findings on these biomarkers [e.g., antioxidant enzymes] are clear indications of possible health implications."[49]

A 2010 study found that EMF induced excess production of ROS in the cells that eventually become muscle.[50] This study identified that EMF could lead to damage in muscle cells that are being formed.

Warning

Potential Health Effects – on muscle cells:

> Any muscle group in the body could be affected, including skeletal or valuable heart muscle cells.

These studies identify that part of the damage that EMF radiation is capable of producing is due to an increase in free radicals or ROS. These increases could overwhelm and consume the body's normal levels of antioxidants, which serve as a protective system to neutralize the damage that occurs from the free unpaired electrons in free radicals or ROS. Indeed, a review of the role of excess ROS in the body links them to the:

". . . pathogenesis of cancer, cardiovascular disease, atherosclerosis, hypertension [high blood pressure], ischemia/reperfusion injury [restoration of blood flow to area after deficient blood flow], diabetes mellitus, neurodegenerative diseases (Alzheimer's disease and Parkinson's disease), rheumatoid arthritis, and aging."[51]

How cell phone radiations are being connected to most of these conditions are described throughout this book.

EMF – Affect on DNA

In an article published in 2009, Drs. Martin Blank and Reba Goodman, of Columbia University in New York, identified that EMF in both ELF (extremely low frequency) and radio frequency (RF) radiation ranges interact with DNA inducing a stress response. The RF range induces breaks in the DNA strands as well, causing them to urge that EMF safety limits must be changed.[52]

In 2011, these same researchers determined that DNA acts as an antenna, reacting across a wide EMF frequency range. This interaction between the DNA and the EMF in the environment led them to hypothesize that EMF radiation could be contributing to the increases in cancers that are being seen.[53]

Recreating normal cell phone use, researchers exposed human trophoblast cells (cells that attach a fertilized egg to the uterine wall and become the placenta) to continuous wave (CW) of 1.8 GHz (1800 MHz) for up to 24 hours and found no damage. However, they found different results when exposing them to *pulsing* (non-continuous) radiation. Cells exposed for 16 and 24 hours to 1.8 GHz GSM with intermittent exposure of 5 minutes *on* and 10 minutes *off* had significant increases in DNA damage. (This *on/off* cycle would be closer to how a cell phone is actually utilized.) Removing the damaged cells from the radiation exposure showed that in the absence of radiation there was repair of the damage within 2 hours. The researchers concluded that their data suggest the normal use of 2G GSM phones has the ability to harm our cellular DNA.[54]

This study shows that if the offending radiation is stopped for 2 hours, DNA may be able to repair. The problem with utility smart meters is that there is no relief from the constant transmission. Our utility company's website states that the meters only transmit a few minutes a day. However, they broadcast microbursts in a *pulse* fashion once or more every minute to keep the meters synchronized so that a coherent report of the customers' usage information is transmitted to utility companies by the collector or web meters once or twice per day. This continual 24 hour a day exposure allows no time for the DNA breakage that does occur to repair. The previous study demonstrates that CW (continuous wave) transmission does not show damage, while the *pulsing*, intermittent modulated radiation causes damage, which indicates the *pulsing* smart meters have a greater potential of causing harm.

Warning

Potential Health Effects – *pulsing* EMF radiation 24 hours a day:

DNA cannot repair the breaks

Cancers

In a study published in 2013 in *Ecotoxicology and Environmental Safety*, when researchers exposed the DNA of a calf thymus gland to the cell phone frequency of 940 MHz they found that the structure of the DNA was altered, with a change in shape of the DNA, as well as breakages in the strands. Finding that the changes to the DNA were still there over 2 hours later, these researchers identified that the DNA damage to the thymus gland cells was irreversible. They concluded their findings with the warning:

> "Collectively, our results reveal that 940 MHz can alter the structure of DNA. The displacement of electrons in DNA by EMFs may lead to conformational [structural] changes of DNA and DNA disaggregation [separation]. Results from this study could have an important implication on the health effects of RF– EMFs exposure."[55]

Since the thymus gland is central to the body's immunity, any decrease in its functioning would result in increased infections, as well as cancers.

Warning

Potential Health Effects – from 940 MHz cell phone radiation.

Irreversible thymus gland DNA damage:

Cancers
Infections

The following diagram of the vital structures that are within every cell summarizes the effect of electromagnetic radiation on our critically essential DNA, as well as our cellular energy and protein producing structures.

Effects of Electromagnetic Fields at the Cellular Level

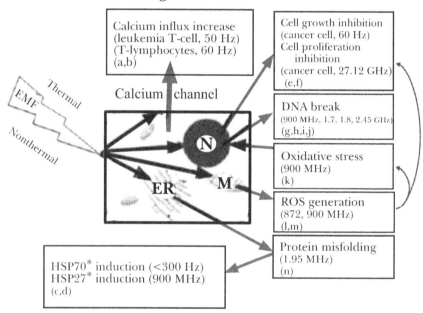

* Heat shock proteins (HSP) = proteins that are produced by cells when subjected to stressful conditions.

Figure 2: Summary of the effects of electromagnetic fields at the cellular level. EMF, electromagnetic field; N, nucleus; ER, endoplasmic reticulum; M, mitochondria.

Source: Gye MC, Park CJ. Effect of electromagnetic field exposure on the reproductive system. *Clin Exp Reprod Med.* 2012;39(1):1-9. (See additional footnotes related to chart built by Gye and Park).[56] Reprinted with permission.

As you can see, almost every vital function that is necessary for the cell to perform in order to maintain life is compromised by EMF radiations.

EMF – Affect on the Blood-brain Barrier

The body is designed to have cells that form protective barriers to prevent toxic chemicals and foreign bacteria from entering the body, especially into our vulnerable brain tissue. To accomplish this, there is a continuous barrier of tight junction cells (TJ) that create what is termed the blood-brain barrier (BBB). A healthy blood-brain barrier (BBB), by regulating the transport of small and large molecules between the blood and the central nervous system (CNS), is essential for protecting the CNS against neurotoxins, and in maintaining optimal levels of essential nutrients and neurotransmitters. These specialized cells perform many functions, including essential communications between the cells.

Tight Junction Cells (TJ)

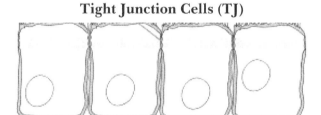

Provides barrier protection throughout the body.

Conflicting results have been published in the past as to whether EMF can cause disruptions in the blood-brain barrier, creating permeable gaps that allow the passage of toxins into the brain.[57] However, the complexity of whether there is an affect or not is dependent on so many variables, it is impossible to design a study that would narrow down and eliminate all the influencing factors. One researcher highlighted the problem that there are too many variables to obtain consistent results by stating:

"Evidence for an effect of the EMF generated by magnetic resonance imaging [MRI] on permeability is conflicting and conclusions are hampered by potential confounders and simultaneous exposure to different types and frequencies of EMF."[58]

However, evidence is mounting that EMF radiation alters the tight junctions of the barriers to such a degree that they no longer form the protective seal that prevents leakage into the brain or from the gut into the blood. This is being proven by studies that are identifying substances that would normally not cross the barriers do so when the cells are exposed to EMF radiation. Studies published in 2001, 2002 and 2005 identified that exposure to 900/915 MHz radiation causes leakage through the blood-brain barrier into the cells surrounding this important barrier that results in brain tissue injury.[59]

In 2003, a group of researchers from Lund University in Sweden published a study in *Environmental Health Perspectives* that identified leakage in the blood-brain barrier and that the leakage created damage in the cells near the leaking. When they exposed rats for 2 hours to the GSM cell phone frequency, leakage was found in the blood-brain barrier in 40% of the animals, which was still demonstrated 8 weeks after the exposure was stopped. They stated that the initial leakage may well lead to secondary blood-brain barrier openings, which could initiate a vicious cycle.

On examining the rat's brains 50 days after exposure, they found highly significant damage to nerve cells in various regions of the brain including the hippocampus, the cortex (outer layer), and basal ganglia (involved with motor and learning functions).[60] The following are the pictures of the brains of the rats from this study.

Brain - no EMF exposure   50 days after one 2 hour expo-
                               sure to GSM phone frequencies

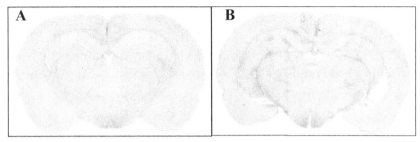

Figure 3. Rat brain-blood brain barrier leakage from one 2 hour
           cell phone exposure.

Source: Salford LG, Brun AE, Eberhardt JL, Malmgren L, Persson
         BR. Nerve cell damage in mammalian brain after exposure to
         microwaves from GSM mobile phones. *Environmental Health
         Perspectives*. 2003;111(7):881-883; discussion A408.
         Reprinted with permission.

Compared to the unexposed brain in photo A, photo B of an EMF
exposed brain shows holes in the blood-brain barrier throughout
the brain, which can easily be identified by the dark areas. These
area are indicative of nerve cell damage where there was leakage
through the barrier.

In studies published in 2008 and 2009, these researchers
exposing rats to 900 MHz for 2 hours, demonstrated an increase
in permeability (leaking) of the blood-brain barrier from this
wavelength. Waiting to see if the tissue repaired after withdrawal
of the radiation, the rats were not sacrificed until 7, 14, and 28
days after exposure. Their brains showed that their cells had
not recovered as there were still signs of leakage of the blood-
brain barrier, as well as damage to the nerve cells. They also
identified that the amount of damage correlated to the amount
of leakage.[61]

These studies show that one exposure of only 2 hours of
EMF radiation, at a normal cell phone frequency, leads to a compromised blood-brain barrier creating nerve cell damage in the
brain. This effect still shows up almost 2 months later, indicating
that it may not be reversible.

A 2015 study confirmed the leakage of the blood-brain barrier from EMF and memory loss due to the exposure. Researchers exposed rats to 900 MHz for 3 hours a day for either 14 or 28 days. The 28 day exposure induced nerve cell damage, and created leakage of the blood-brain barrier. In testing the rats they identified significantly impaired spatial memory, which is the ability to remember the position or location of objects and places.[62]

Warning

Cell phone radiation:

Memory loss

EMF – Affect on Leaky Gut / Digestive Problems

Leaky Gut Syndrome

Tight Junctions in the Intestinal Lining

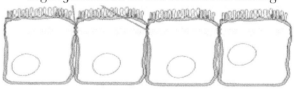

The blood-brain barrier's tight junction cells are similar to those that are necessary to maintain the integrity of the intestinal lining. EMF not only affect the tight junction cells of the blood-brain barrier, they also affect the tight junction cells of the intestinal barrier lining of the gut. The entire intestinal lining of the digestive tract is composed of a continuous protective barrier of tight junction cells. Their function in the GI tract is to prevent infectious organisms and only partially digested food particles from entering into the body's blood stream. The same increase in leaking that occurs in the blood-brain barrier due to EMF radiation, also opens up the cells in the gut resulting in food particles being released into the blood. Termed "leaky gut," the food particles can create allergic reactions, and reactions that can also lead to autistic behavioral problems.

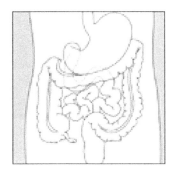

Warning

Potential Health Effects – impact on intestinal lining creating leaky gut:

Food Allergies
Altered behavioral responses

Wi-Fi Radiation – Affects All Living Cells

EMF – Wi-Fi Effect
The Garden Cress Seed Experiment

Experiments with garden cress seeds and the classroom's Wi-Fi router by a 9th Grade class in Denmark gained International attention when they won a prize for their experiment (May 16, 2013). The students became sick at school where they had Wi-Fi and were not sick at home where they did not have Wi-Fi. So they decided to see what effect their Wi-Fi router would have on simple garden cress seeds. The following picture on the left shows seeds that were in the room with a Wi-Fi router, while the picture on the right is of seeds grown in a room away from the Wi-Fi router. As the pictures show, Wi-Fi radiation has a detrimental effect on living cells. If viewing this in book format of black and white, the picture on the left shows dead, brown seeds. The picture on the right as eBook readers can see has lush green growth.[63]

Garden Cress Seeds – 12 Days Grow

In room with
the Wi-Fi router

One room away from
the Wi-Fi router

Dead seeds

Flourishing seeds

Reprinted with permission.

These pictures *clearly* show how Wi-Fi radiation affects all life.

[There are devices available that can harmonize the radiation
that EMF electronics emit, including Wi-Fi routers.
See page 227 for our recommendations.]

Part 2

Body-wide Effects

Electromagnetic Sensitivity Symptoms

- Headaches / Migraines / Short breath
- Insomnia / Difficulty sleeping
- Heart palpitations
- Behavior disorders / Irritability
- Tinnitus (ringing in ears)
- Vertigo / Dizziness / Nausea
- Blurred vision
- Fatigue
- Food allergies
- Memory loss / Brain fog
- Bleeding / Nose bleeds
- Numbness in extremities
- Skin rashes / Tingling / Itching
- Nerve / Muscle pain / Contractions
- Lyme disease like symptoms

Chapter 5

Electromagnetic Radiation Symptoms

Biochemical Proof They Are Real

It is important to address the fact that approximately 2 – 20% of people state they suffer symptoms when exposed to EMF radiation from cell phones, Wi-Fi, and computers. These people are said to be electromagnetic sensitive (EMS) or have electromagnetic hypersensitivity (EHS). Up until now it has been difficult to scientifically prove that the EMF radiations are responsible for their headaches, skin rashes, insomnia, and heart palpitations. The problem with designing studies for validating EHS symptoms is that it is difficult to measure:

1. A subjective feeling, like a headache.
2. Something that cannot be seen.
3. Something that cannot be fully measured with today's technology.

The body is more sensitive than any meter or safety limit. What is important is how the body reacts to the EMF stimuli. The studies that need to be developed are those that are able to register changes EMF radiation creates at the biochemical level of the cell. Since this is difficult to accomplish, studies have been published that do not support the claims of those who are hypersensitive.

In a January 2013 article published in *Electromagnetic Biology and Medicine*, Drs. Tuengler and von Klitzing hypothesized that there are objective ways to measure whether a person is electromagnetic hypersensitive. Using the objective measurable parameters of heart rate variability, microcirculation in the capillaries, and electrical potential in the skin, they are able to identify those who are EMF hypersensitive. They emphasize:

"The vulnerable group of people suffering from electromagnetic hypersensitivity should no longer be neglected or stigmatized only because there is no accepted model of effect of this condition."[64]

Citing the research that identifies *pulsing* radiation has more of an effect than continuous radiation exposure; and that it is a combination of stressors that show effects when one by itself may not, Drs. Tuengler and von Klitzing in the following paragraph urge that these early warning signs exhibited by those suffering with electromagnetic sensitivity should be heeded.[65]

"Many years of research into athermal [non heating] effects not only brought about more knowledge, but also more sources of uncertainty and ignorance. This may be due to the complexity of interaction of electromagnetic fields with biological systems and the variety of methodology used. Nevertheless it cannot be denied that those athermal effects exist. In fact they seem to profoundly affect living systems. We are only at the beginning of understanding those complex interactions. And that should pave the way to more research but at the same time not hinder us from being more cautious in respect to exposure to electromagnetic fields. We should not follow the principle of 'paralysis by analysis' [do nothing while over-analyzing] but instead heed the early warnings."[66]

The evidence of the health hazards of EMF throughout this book highlights the need for the world to pay attention to these researchers' words of warning.

Smart Meter Health Effects Survey
(Sponsored by Maine Coalition to
Stop Smart Meters and www.conradbiologic.com)

A survey written and conducted by Richard Conrad, Ph.D, and Ed Friedman was designed to discover if the symptoms many people have recently been attributing to exposures from smart meters were really caused by those exposures or not. As a Maine smart meter activist preparing evidence for a state investigation into the health and safety of the meters, Friedman knew he would face standard utility claims that smart meter symptoms were psychosomatic. Having heard from hundreds of citizens having similar adverse reactions to meter installations and having read a great deal of the science on radiofrequency (RF) radiation exposure he realized: ". . . there were too many people in too many places with too many variables associated with their lives, and what I was seeing seemed impossible to fit with a psychological response. In fact the only common denominator appeared to be the smart meters." So Friedman and Conrad designed a survey to answer the question whether people's symptoms were real or psychosomatic. They found 42% of survey respondents began suffering symptoms at or after smart meter installation but *before* they knew a meter had been installed. Of the 210 respondents, there were about a dozen common symptoms that correlate with those previously reported in the literature.[67]

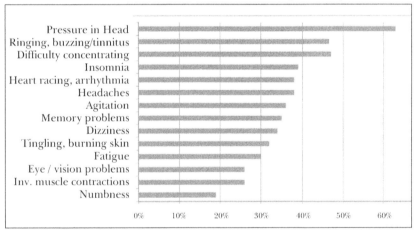

New Symptoms from Smart Meters
Severe and Moderate Combined (N=210)

Figure 4. Smart meter survey symptoms.

Source: Conrad R, Friedman E. Maine Coalition to Stop Smart Meters (www.mainecoalitiontostopsmartmeters.org). Chart credit: Friedman E, [chart derived from Appendix 3, Smart Meter Health Effects Survey & Report. Unpublished material, chart received via personal communication from Ed Friedman.] Reprinted with permission.

The Maine smart meter survey identifies that 20 – 60% of the survey respondents express that they feel symptoms when they are around smart meters. The results of the scientific studies described in this book verify what these people are feeling is very real and very debilitating.

When looking at the changes within living cells when they are exposed to electromagnetic radiation, each of the symptoms have a biochemical basis for their occurring. This chapter will cover the scientific evidence for what people are feeling in their homes and work environments. These are not psychosomatic symptoms. The symptoms need to be recognized, along with making changes in the environment, so electromagnetic sensitive people can stay in their homes and on their jobs, allowing them to remain productive members of society.

Electromagnetic Sensitivity Symptoms Survey in Progress

Beatrice Golomb, M.D., Ph.D. of the UC San Diego Golomb Research Group has an open research study asking for electrohypersensitive (EHS) affected and unaffected people to participate. EMF is known to cause oxidative stress (cell damage) and mitochondrial injury, which are the focus of Dr. Golomb's research. The survey, which will be followed by research on EHS biomarkers, asks about risk factors, mechanisms and effects of EHS. To make a change, we need documentation, please participate – even those without symptoms as you are needed as baseline controls (normal population). The 2023 website to download the survey is: www.GolombResearchGroup.org

Headaches

EMF – Affect on Headache

Red Blood Cells (RBC)

Alteration of the electrical charge on the cell membrane results in changes in the RBC. It is normally smooth and doughnut shaped (as seen in the picture below), which is the ideal shape for it to carry its maximum supply of oxygen throughout the body. Live analyses on blood exposed to cell phone radiation show the red blood cells assume a more spherical shape with spikes or thorns over their surface. They also are attracted to each other and stick together in a pattern that is termed rouleaux.[68] Changing the shape of the red blood cell, along with its clumping rouleaux formation,

Normal shaped
red blood cells

leads to the cell's inability to carry its normal and necessary amount of oxygen to the tissues throughout the body.

The following are samples of human blood taken after:

1. Exposure to today's average environment.
2. One hour of exposure to a cell phone.
3. One hour of exposure to a cell phone with an EMF mitigation device attached, which is programmed to harmonize the cell phone's energy field.

Sample 1 – Live red blood cell analysis:
Taken on arrival – average blood before cell phone exposure.

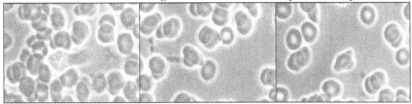

Sample 2 – Live red blood cell analysis:
After 1 hour of cell phone EMF exposure.

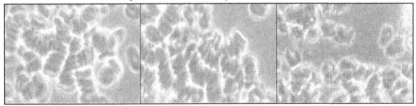

Sample 3 – Live red blood cell analysis:
After 1 hour of cell phone use with an EMF mitigating device.

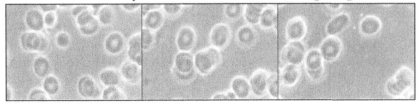

Figure 5. Red blood cells with and without cell phone exposure. [Details regarding products used are described on pages 229 - 234.]

Source: The Effects of the Electrodot Electromagnetic Harmonizer on Live Blood Following Exposure to EMFs (independent research conducted for Phi Harmonics LTD, Devon, UK—unpublished). Layfield P. Reprinted with permission.

Sample 1: Some of the red blood cells stick together, which is called rouleaux. This identifies there is a background of EMF radiation today that everyone is exposed to that alters our red blood cell membranes.

Sample 2: It is easy to identify the increase in rouleaux. Red blood cells that are stuck together cannot supply the oxygen our tissues need. The low oxygen environment leads to headaches and shortness of breath. It is the same as the headache that occurs in the low oxygen environment at high altitudes. The headache pain makes some people seek lower elevations as quickly as possible.

Additionally, red blood cells have to pass through tiny capillaries single file in a folded-over manner. When they stick together it is difficult for them to pass through the body's tiny capillaries, and they can cause breakage of the capillaries or form blood clots.

Sample 3: It is clear that the harmonizing effect of an EMF mitigating device resulted in maintaining the correct charge on the red blood cells, which allows them to separate and return to their normal shape, so they can perform their critical function of delivering oxygen to all the tissues throughout the body. Even though the individual was on a cell phone for 1 hour, his red blood cells regained normal size and functioning. Please note that this is an improvement over the blood cells exposed to what has become our normal background radiation shown in Sample 1. [Products used are described on pages 229 - 234.]

Other researchers have confirmed the impact of EMF on red blood cells. When they exposed RBCs to 900 MHz, they found the blood cells do have significant changes in their shape and size and concluded:

"The results of this study may be significant on protection of human beings and other living organisms against possible radiation affections of the high-frequency electromagnetic waves."[69]

These significant changes in red blood cells shape in size, resulting in their loss of fluidity (ability to flow freely), are why they cannot deliver their life-saving oxygen. The changes not only account for the headaches people get from the reduced oxygen to their brain, but also the increase in cancers that are being seen. Oncologists state cancer arises in a low oxygen, high blood sugar environment. EMF radiation is also found to raise blood sugar, which is discussed later in this book.

Warning

Potential Health Effects:

Not enough oxygen to the brain = Headaches
Not enough oxygen to the cells = Shortness of breath
Low oxygen in tissues   = Promotion of cancer

An additional reason for people developing headaches is the evidence that a breakdown in the blood-brain barrier could lead to the development of headaches.[70] (EMF radiation compromising the BBB was discussed earlier in the section on EMF – Affect on the Blood-brain Barrier.)

EMF – Affect on Anemia

Many people in the United States are being diagnosed with anemia today, with doctors stating they cannot determine the cause. Anemia is the result of not enough of the oxygen carrying hemoglobin, which is what comprises red blood cells. Oxygen attaches to the hemoglobin of the RBCs while in the lungs, then they circulate throughout the body transporting the life giving oxygen to the tissues.

From the live previously shown, you can see the misshaped RBCs become spherical in shape when exposed to cell phone or computer EMF radiation. The spleen's function is to remove abnormally shaped RBCs from circulation. Researchers have found that RBCs with reduced surface area are rapidly and completely entrapped in the spleen.[71] It is possible that the spleen recognizing the radiation created misshaped RBCs is removing them from circulation.

People exposed continually to computers and cell phones, with the resultant change in RBC shape could lose a proportion of their RBCs, which would result in an anemic presentation of not enough hemoglobin to carry oxygen. Many of the symptoms of anemia that arise from not enough oxygen in the tissues are very similar to those expressed by people who are exposed to cell phone or smart meter radiation. They are:

Easy fatigue and loss of energy
Unusually rapid heartbeat, particularly with exercise
Shortness of breath and headache, particularly with exercise
Difficulty concentrating
Dizziness
Insomnia
Pale skin
Leg cramps.[72]

It is important to consider that some electromagnetic hypersensitivity (EHS) symptoms are caused by the inability of RBCs to deliver their full supply of oxygen. Researchers have identified that rats exposed to 900 MHz radiation showed oxidation damage to the red blood cells. The damage would result in their not being able to transport oxygen. In testing the antioxidant properties of vitamin C, they found it prevented the oxidation damage in the group of rats given vitamin C. Whereas, this was not seen in the EMF exposed group that did not receive the vitamin C.[73] With results like this, it may be that people with less antioxidants, like vitamin C, in their bodies are the ones who are experiencing EHS symptoms.

EMF – Affect on White Blood Cells, and Platelets

White Blood Cells and Platelets Change Count

A study published in 2012 identified that both red and white blood cells, as well as platelets are broken after exposure to cell phone radiation. They also identified that there is an accompanying change in the fluidity of the blood.[74] This can be the result of the change in the charge on their surfaces, which makes the red blood cells stick together, as previously shown in Sample 2 and account for the blood being less fluid. The breakage of the red blood cells would also result in the spleen removing them from circulation, leading to symptoms of anemia as discussed in the previous section.

When investigators exposed rabbits to 950 MHz, for 2 hours a day for 2 weeks, they concluded:

"Results of this study suggest that the two main groups of blood cells which are leukocytes [white blood cells] and thrombocytes [platelets] are disturbed as a result of mobile phone EMF exposure. So, it is possible that this kind of electromagnetic field could affect constant cell counts of peripheral blood [blood that circulates in the blood vessels]. Signals transmitted by a mobile phone, even if it is a hands-free, will reach all parts of the body including bone marrow, lymphoid organs and circulatory system."[75]

This conclusion identifies that cell phones radiate the entire body, not just the areas they are held against. In addition, a 2015 article identifies that platelets are subject to oxidative stress and decrease in their oxygen metabolism upon their exposure to LCD monitors.[76] Some people today are bleeding into their tissues showing red/purple splotches in their skin to the same degree as those who take a blood thinners. Since EMF oxidize and reduce platelet numbers, this type of bleeding could also arise due to cell phone or computer radiation exposure. Normal, healthy concentrations of platelets are necessary to prevent excessive bleeding.

Warning

Potential Health Effects – on blood cells:

Decreased, oxidized platelets = bleeding disorders, nosebleeds

Decreased white blood cells = decreased immunity to diseases

EMF – Alter White Blood Cells Behavior

Our white blood cells (WBCs) help the body defend against infections and cancer. Changing their behavior could result in decreased ability to defend against either of these outcomes. A change in their behavior is what researchers found when exposing WBCs to 1800 MHz RF radiation with a SAR of 1.25 W/kg, which is within the safety guideline recommendations of the FCC in the United States. When placing the WBC at a distance of 5 centimeters from the microscope stage, the average time for the WBCs exposed to RF radiation response was 2.5 minutes. The radiation also resulted in the cells moving in parallel with the mobile phone position. In addition, they displayed significant changes in their behavior, including changing shape much faster, along with shrinking, expanding, and rolling. The following is a summary of their findings.

White Blood Cell Behavior from 1800 MHz / SAR 1.25 W/kg

Cell behavior	Without RF radiation	With RF radiation
Cell response time constant to RF radiation:	The cells act normally	Delayed 2.5 minutes
Average movement speed:	3.45 μm/min*	6.40 μm/min*
Changing shape:	Normal	Faster
Movement direction:	Sideward direction	Upward direction

* μm/min = micrometers per minute.

Figure 6. Cell behavior upon radiation exposure.

Source: Aly AA, Deris S, Zaki N. The Effects on Cells Mobility Due to Exposure to EMF Radiation. *Advanced Computing: An International Journal (ACIJ).* 2011 July;2(4). Reprinted with permission.

In addition, one of the significant results they found was that RF radiation caused damage to the leukocytes cells from certain blood where the cells expanded and lost their ability to move.

The body's WBCs dramatic change in behavior upon exposure to electrical radiation could be responsible for decreased immunity. It may also help explain why studies over the years have linked electromagnetic radiation (EMR) to increase in leukemia (abnormal, out of control WBCs), which has been seen particularly in children.[77]

Warning

Potential Health Effects – altered white blood cells behavior:

Decreased immunity

Increased cancers

Insomnia

EMF – Affect on Sleep / Insomnia

One of the symptoms that people often report after smart meters are installed in their neighborhoods is insomnia. In fact, some people state they had to move out of their homes and into their cars before they could sleep. Without proper sleep, the body begins to malfunction on many levels.

In looking at EMF and sleep, a study published in 2012 that exposed 30 human volunteers to *pulse* modulated 900 MHz radiation for 30 minutes before sleep found a difference in the deepest most restorative sleep—the rapid eye movement stage. They stated:

> "Consistent with our previous findings, our results provide further evidence that *pulse* modulated RF (radio frequency) EMF alter brain physiology . . ."[78]

One of the reasons it has been difficult to grasp the idea that EMF radiation is harmful is that not all people are being affected immediately, as the symptoms develop from the accumulation of the radiation, and eventually appear when the body cannot handle the stress of the radiation any longer. It is difficult for people who are not being impacted by any of the symptoms that are presented in this book to understand and believe the symptoms of those who are. This study highlights the differences in reaction as they only had 30 men in this sleep study, yet they found:

> "Importantly, this exposure-induced effect showed considerable individual variability."[79]

In a 2012 article looking at EMF affect on sleep and feeding habits, rats exposed to chronic 900 MHz RF–EMF exposure for 5 weeks had significantly lower tail temperatures than controls at all sleep stages. The researchers theorized blood vessels constricting was the body's energy saving response.[80] It may be the lower tail temperature is the result of rouleauxed red blood cells inability to flow through the tail's small capillaries to deliver blood and oxygen.

Melatonin and Sleep

Melatonin is a hormone that is well known for its function in assisting with obtaining the deep reparative sleep the human body needs, which is especially important now to repair the damage that is occurring in everyone due to our constant 24 hour a day exposure to many EMF frequencies. Melatonin is very involved in the regulation of the onset and the quality of sleep. In a 2004 review on the affect of EMF on cellular functions, some studies identified that exposure to 50 – 60 Hz (household current) can inhibit the effects of melatonin.[81]

Cell phone and microwave radiations, that are the same frequency as utility smart meters, are also found to decrease melatonin. Researchers in studies published in 2011 and 2012 exposed rats to 900 MHz and to 2.45 GHz (2450 MHz) for 2 hours a day for 45 days and found the rats demonstrated a significant decrease in melatonin to both frequencies.

Cell Phone / Microwave Radiations Decrease Melatonin

Rats	900 MHz Cell Phone	2.45 GHz Microwave
Sham (no exposure)	85.20 ng/mg*	81.03 ng/mg*
Exposed	66.21 ng/mg*	53.66 ng/mg*

* ng/mg protein = nanograms per milligram protein

Source: Kesari KK, Kumar S, Behari J. 900-MHz microwave radiation promotes oxidation in rat brain. *Electromagn Biol Med.* 2011;30(4):219–234.

Kesari KK, Kumar S, Behari J. Pathophysiology of microwave radiation: effect on rat brain. *Appl Bioochem Biotechnol.* 2012;166(2):379-388.

Another study discussed later in this book also identifies that EMF exposure decreases melatonin.[82] This reduction in melatonin levels could be one reason people state that they developed insomnia when utility smart meters (which emit the same 2.45 GHz frequency) were installed in their neighborhoods.

Warning
Potential Health Effects – decreased melatonin:
Insomnia
Reduced deep restorative sleep

Melatonin also has antioxidative effects that protect cell membranes. Hormones work when they attach to their specific receptors in the cells where their action is needed. Melatonin plays many roles throughout the body, as melatonin receptors have been found not only in the brain, but also in the retina of the eye, cardiovascular system, liver, gallbladder, intestines, kidney, immune cells, fat cells, prostate and breast epithelial cells, ovary/granulosa* cells, uterine lining, as well as the skin. Having reduced levels of melatonin due to cell phone and wireless exposure could have many consequences considering it is found in almost every organ, which reveals it performs important roles for each organ system's optimal functioning.[83]

* Granulosa cells – a hormone producing cell within the ovarian egg follicle.

Heart Palpitations

EMF – Affect on Heart Palpitations / Arrhythmia / Racing

Researchers have confirmed that even healthy subjects who have not been identified with electromagnetic sensitivity show significant changes in heart rate variability from cell phones. They exposed 32 healthy students to a 1.8 MHz GSM cell phone for 20 minute intervals before, during, and after cell phone use and measured their heart rate with a Holter Monitor*. Every student showed significant changes in heart rate variability (arrhythmia) from before phone use, during phone use, and for the 20 minutes following the call.[84]

* Holter monitor: a portable device used to measure the electrical activity of the heart over an extended period of time, allowing detection of intermittent arrhythmias and other electrical disturbances.[85]

Other researchers looked at the effects of the common 900 MHz radiation from mobile phones on the heart rate variability (HRV) of healthy young volunteers. They used the cell phones in the following two modes:

Very low EMF = phone in stand-by
Higher EMF   = phone in pre-ring signal exchange and
                 phone ringing.

Mathematically, the researchers identified the higher EMF mode creates significantly greater chaos in the heart rate variability. The researchers concluded:

"Consequently, we have concluded that high level EMF changed the complexity of cardiac system behavior, significantly."[86]

Many people today are seeing their doctors due to these irregular heartbeats. Holter monitors are identifying the arrhythmias that are occurring due to EMF exposure, leading to some having pacemakers implanted. It is important to rule out radiation exposure as a cause before this invasive, life changing procedure is considered.

Another way that EMF radiation can affect heart function is through their alteration of mast cells. Mast cells contain granules that open upon EMF exposure and spill their contents into the tissues. (See picture in section on EMF – Affect on Itching / Tingling / Burning Skin / Rashes.) Mast cells are present in the heart tissue and studies made on interactions of EMF with the cardiac function have demonstrated changes are present in the heart after exposure to EMF, which could also be due to mast cells degranulation after exposure to EMF.[87]

EMF – Affect on Blood Pressure
Not only do EMF create changes in heartbeat, they also raise blood pressure (BP). Researchers worked with healthy volunteers between 26 and 36 years of age, exposing them for 35 minutes to 900 MHz cell phone attached to their head. A remote control was used so that the volunteers did not know whether the phone was on or off. EMF exposure created a significant

increase in blood pressure at rest, and after standing. By measuring capillary pressure, they determined that there was also significantly more pronounced vasoconstriction (narrowing of blood vessels) upon EMF exposure. Based on their findings, the researchers stated:

> "We conclude that exposure of the right hemisphere to a radio-frequency EMF for 35 minutes causes an increase in sympathetic efferent activity with increases in resting BP between 5 and 10 mm Hg, most likely due to more pronounced vasoconstriction [narrowing of blood vessels]."[88]

With studies revealing many types of effects on the heart and circulation, EMF radiation could have considerable affect on heart disease. Researchers seeing the results of many studies that identify all the damage that EMF radiation can create within the cells and throughout the body are publishing articles of warning. Just the titles of these articles such as: *Mobile phones: time to rethink and limit usage* herald that everyone needs to decide if the convenience of electronic technology is worth the health problems that can develop, and occur at much younger ages than humanity has ever seen.[89]

Irritability

EMF – Affect on Behavior: Arousal / Irritability / Emotionality

Cerebellum Cell Loss

Purkinje cells are large branching nerve cells in the brain's cerebellum (back region of brain controlling movement and balance). The cells release gamma-aminobutyric acid (GABA), the brain's most predominant neurotransmitter that inhibits or reduces the transmission of nerve impulses.

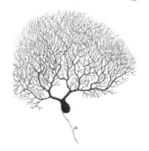

Purkinje Cell

A study on rats exposed to the cell phone frequency of 900 MHz for 1 hour a day for 28 days found they had a significant decrease in the number of these critically important Purkinje cells in the cerebellum.[90] Other researchers working with mice exposed to the 890 – 915 MHz cell phone frequencies also found a decreased number of Purkinje cells.[91]

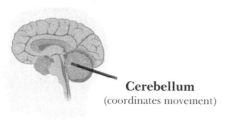

Cerebellum
(coordinates movement)

Researchers looking at prenatal EMF exposure on the cerebellum of rat offspring, exposed pregnant rats to 900 MHz *pulse* radiation for 6 hours a day during the whole gestation (pregnancy) period. Purkinje neuron cells in the cerebellum revealed altered electrophysiological properties with decreased excitability of the nerve cells in rats exposed to EMF. Their conclusion was that electromagnetic field (EMF) radiations emitted from mobile phones may cause structural damage to neurons (nerve cells).[92]

The neurotransmitter GABA that Purkinje cells release is involved in many functions. It is important for relaxation and for sleep, and is also critical in regulating and coordinating motor movements.[93] The findings from these studies confirm there should be further studying of people suffering from motor coordination deficits, such as Parkinson's disease patients. They may be affected by EMF radiation that is decreasing the number of Purkinje cells, thereby impairing GABA transmission in their brains.

Warning

Potential Health Effects – decreased Purkinje cells:

Parkinson's disease
Motor coordination deficits

Children are beginning to demonstrate motor coordination deficits. In a 2014 article published in the United Kingdom's *The Guardian*, teachers were voicing their concerns that: "Children can swipe a screen but can't use toy building blocks, teachers warn."[94] In looking at what is different, they thought it may be that the children have no practice at things like block building any more. With the proof that EMF radiation kills the cells in the brain that are necessary for fine motor coordination, then cell phones and Wi-Fi radiation, including the iPads that are being distributed to thousands of school children around the world, need to be reconsidered until they can be proven they are not injuring children's rapidly developing brains.

GABA is an inhibitory neurotransmitter, meaning that it reduces excitatory responses by essentially putting the brakes on. As one of the body's primary avenues of promoting relaxation, it provides the ability to stay peaceful and calm, and it is also important in reducing stress. Reduced GABA activity is identified in children who are diagnosed with attention deficit hyperactivity disorder (ADHD).[95]

A study published in 2008 looked at over 13,000 mothers and their children who were measured both prenatally (during pregnancy) and postnatally (after delivery) for exposure to cell phone radiation. They identified that there was a higher score for overall behavioral problems in the children who were exposed to cell phone use, either during fetal development or postnatally from birth to 7 years-old. They concluded:

"Exposure to cell phones prenatally—and, to a lesser degree, postnatally—was associated with behavioral difficulties such as emotional and hyperactivity problems around the age of school entry."[96]

Four years later in 2012, these same researchers examined the results of a larger, different group of children to see if they obtained the same results. In looking at over 28,000 children, they again found there were behavioral problems at age 7 years-old in those children who had both prenatal and postnatal exposure to cell phone radiation.[97]

It is critical to protect the fetus throughout pregnancy as these studies indicate that EMF radiation exposure may cause alterations in fetal programming, one result of which may be in altered behavior patterns.

Warning

Potential Health Effects – reduced GABA:

Irritability
Hyperactivity
ADHD
Autism

In 2010, other researchers reviewed 10 studies that assessed possible health effects for those living near cell towers (mobile phone base stations). Studying the association between health issues and the closeness to base antennas, 7 examined neurobehavioral effects and 3 investigated cancer. They found 8 of the 10 studies reported increases in adverse neurobehavioral symptoms, or cancer in people living less than 1,600 feet (500 meters) from the cell towers. Since all of the studies reported exposure levels below accepted international guidelines, the investigators stated that these results suggest that the current guidelines are not adequate enough to protect human health. They concluded:

> "We believe that comprehensive epidemiological [the study of disease in populations] studies of long-term mobile phone base station exposure are urgently required to more definitively understand its health impact."[98]

One explanation for the neurobehavioral problems identified in these studies is disruption of the production of GABA. In looking at loss of GABA functioning (due to decreased Purkinje cells), recent studies have found that abnormal functioning of GABA producing nerve cells plays a role in many neuropsychiatric disorders, which includes altered social behaviors, such as those found in people with autism and Rett syndrome (a neurodevelopmental disorder that is part of the autism spectrum).[99]

Warning

Potential Health Effects – living near cell towers/base stations:

Neurobehavioral problems
Cancers

Ear Ringing

EMF – Affect on Tinnitus / Ringing or Buzzing Tone in Ears

Many people over the last several years have expressed they have been bothered by tinnitus (ringing the ears), especially after utility smart meters were installed in their neighborhoods. Studies back up this symptom from EMF radiation. The studies throughout this book have identified that EMF exposure disrupts normal GABA activity. A study on mice demonstrates that the reduced inhibitory action of GABA can be responsible for the ringing, since the mice that experienced decreased GABA functioning, displayed evidence of tinnitus.[100]

Warning

Potential Health Effects – decreased GABA functioning:

Tinnitus

In matching 100 human tinnitus patients with control subjects, researchers determined that there is a significantly elevated risk for developing tinnitus with prolonged use of a mobile phone for over 4 years (OR 1.95 – 95% increase). Their results led them to conclude that cell phones should be investigated as a potential risk factor for developing tinnitus.[101]

EMF – Potential Hearing Loss

Reviews of studies performed to determine if EMF radiations produce harm in the body have been concluding that the studies saying there is harm are counterbalanced with the studies claiming they find no harm, and lead to the conclusion there is not enough evidence to claim EMF radiation is a threat to our health.

Reviews of the medical literature can only be as good as the studies that have been published. Some studies are performed for such short periods, there is no way to determine whether the typical long hours and many years of use of EMF radiations effect the body's tissues. Consequently, reviews that include those that have not been performed over a long enough time to detect changes, nullify the results of those that identified harmful changes, resulting in the conclusions that EMF radiation is not creating harm.

A 2005 published study citing that there is only limited knowledge of a cell phone's effect on auditory function stated: "The aim of the study was to assess potential changes in hearing function as a consequence of exposure to low-intensity EMF's produced by mobile phones at frequencies of 900 and 1800 MHz." The length of time of exposure was only a 10-minute close exposure of EMFs emitted from a mobile phone, and they stated that a cell phone had no immediate after-effect on young human subjects and no measurable hearing deterioration was detected in our study.[102]

Two years later, another study was published that established there was no effect on auditory brainstem response upon a single 10 minute exposure to 900 MHz cell phone EMF radiation. They stated: "The aim of the present study was to advance our understanding of potential adverse effects of the GSM mobile phones on the human hearing system."[103] The study could not possibly reveal effects when no one today uses a phone for only 10 minutes.

Other researchers made the exposure for 30 minutes and concluded: ". . . that 30 minutes mobile phone use has no short-term adverse effects on the human auditory system."[104]

When comparing men who used a cellular phone frequently (approximately 2 hours a day for 4 years), to men who were moderate users (10 – 20 minutes a day for 4 years), and a control group of men who have never used a cellular phone, no differences were observed between moderate mobile phone users (10 – 20 minutes per day) and the control subjects. However, these two groups were significantly different than the frequent users who talked approximately 2 hours a day. Based on their findings, the researchers concluded: "This study shows that a higher degree of hearing loss is associated with long-term exposure to electromagnetic (EM) field generated by cellular phones."[105]

When unable to find subjects that had not used a cell phone, investigators decided to study the difference in hearing between the dominant ear they used to listen to their cell phones and their non-dominant ear, which they did not use for their cell phone. Studying 100 subjects that were 53% males and 47% females with an average age of 27, they concluded that chronic mobile phone usage revealed high frequency hearing loss in the dominant ear (mobile phone used) compared to the non-dominant ear that was not exposed to the cell phone.[106] This is of great concern. With young adults of 27 already showing hearing loss from the use of the cell phone, how much hearing loss will they have by the time they reach 60 or 70 years of age?

When the studies look at a length of time of use that matches how people are using cell phones, the results do indicate that cell phone use can create damage to hearing with the typical long term use. Over 100 long-term mobile phone users (more than 1 year) and 50 controls who had never used a mobile phone underwent a battery of audiologic investigations. Trends for audiologic abnormalities were seen within the cell phone users. High-frequency hearing loss was seen with increasing length of time of phone use, excessive use of cell phones, and in those who were more than 30 years old. These changes led the researchers to conclude that: "Long-term and intensive mobile phone use may cause inner ear damage."[107]

EMF – Affect on Dizziness / Vertigo / Nausea

Since the inner ear is involved in maintaining our balance and equilibrium, changes to the ear and inner ear damage that is identified as being caused by cell phone radiation could be a contributing factor of the symptoms some people experience of vertigo, dizziness, and unsteadiness while walking.

When exposing rabbits for 15, 45, and 60 minutes to 900 MHz, researchers did find changes in their auditory pathway that made them state: ". . . exposure to electromagnetic fields emitted by mobile phone can affect the normal electrophysiological activity of the auditory system, and these findings fit the pattern of general responses to a stressor."[108]

Researchers compared auditory brainstem responses of people with typical use of mobile phones. When comparing those who had a history of cell phone use for a maximum 30 minutes a day for 5 years to a control group, they found no difference in their responses. However, in the group that stated they had used mobile phones for 10 years for a maximum of 30 minutes a day, they did find changes, and concluded: "Based on our findings we concluded that long term exposure to mobile phones may affect conduction in the peripheral portion of the auditory pathway [outer, middle, and inner ear]." They recommended that: ". . . more research needs to be done to study the long term effects of mobile phones particularly with the newer technologies like smartphones and 3G."[109]

We have been receiving reports from many who cannot hold the new more powerful 4G phones. Part of the problem with the research today is that technology is advancing so rapidly that by the time a study is published, it is no longer relevant to the technology that is currently in use. These researchers had not looked at smartphones with 3G, and yet technology has even moved past that to 4G, and will even surpass that to 5G.

Blurred Vision

EMF – Affect on Blurred Vision

One of the symptoms people report they experience upon exposure to wireless devices, and after smart meters are installed in their neighborhood, is difficulty with blurry vision.

One of the symptoms of cataracts is blurry vision. Studies reveal that microwaves can lead to lens clouding and the formation of cataracts. These cataracts arise in a different region of the lens of the eye compared to ionizing radiation caused by X-rays, and can be directly related to the power of the microwave, and the length of the exposure to EMF radiation. Their formation is associated with damage to the lens cell membrane, and the DNA within the cells. Researchers in 1988 recommended mechanical shielding from these microwaves and ionizing radiations to minimize the possibility of development of radiation-induced cataracts.[110]

In 2008, investigating the effect on the eye of 1.1 GHz radiation for 15 days, researchers found reversible decrease in lens optical quality accompanied by irreversible structural and biochemical damage to the lens epithelial cell layer. Observing that the lens damage by EMF was distinctly different from that produced by conductive heat, they concluded that electromagnetic fields from microwave radiation have a negative impact on the eye lens.[111]

In 2007, investigations revealed that cell phone exposure creates oxidative stress in the tissue of the cornea and the lens. The study also identified that the antioxidant effect from vitamin C is successful in preventing the EMF radiation damage to the eye tissues (the same as for red blood cells discussed earlier).[112]

The researchers also looked at whether the radiation emitted by a computer monitor has the ability to cause oxidation damage to cornea and lens tissues. They found the monitor did cause oxidation in the lens, but not the cornea, and that the antioxidant properties of vitamin C prevents the oxidation damage in the lens.[113]

A 2007 study is important for those who wear metal framed eyeglasses. This research identified that there is an increase in the amount of radiation that is absorbed for those wearing metal frame glasses. In addition, the levels of radiation created in the metal frame were higher than the established safety limit. The investigators stated their results suggested that the radiation from the cell phone handset has a more harmful effect on the eyes when a person uses glasses with a metal frame.[114]

These studies proving EMF radiation causes oxidation damage to the lens and cornea identify why some people are having problems with blurry vision today. Sadly, this damage from EMF radiation has been identified since the 1980s, yet proliferation of EMF emitting devices continued without warnings.

Fatigue

EMF – Affect on ATP – Fatigue

ATP (adenosine triphosphate) is the main energy molecule of the body's cells. A reduction of our ATP supply would leave us feeling tired and exhausted. This is what many report they are feeling after working for hours in front of a computer screen. Some relate they have trouble even holding their heads up at the end of the day of working in an office.

Adenylate energy charge (AEC) is another measure of energy status. Measurement of AEC is utilized as it is a very sensitive reflection of the energy state of cells. Researchers exposed tomato plants to 900 MHz EMF for 15, 30, and 60 minutes and measured their ATP and AEC concentrations. Both the ATP and AEC were unchanged after 15 minutes, but both were changed after 30 minutes. An organism's normal AEC values are in the range of 0.8 – 0.9, and the plants in this study that were shielded from the EMF had a normal value of 0.84. After 30 minutes, the AEC of EMF exposed plants displayed a 30% decrease from this value. At 60 minutes the value was at 0.63, which the researchers state is extremely low for actively growing tissue. The ATP (a cell's crucial supplier of energy) dropped 40% at 30 minutes, and remained at that level after 60 minutes.

Exposure to 30 minutes of 900 MHz EMF:
- ATP dropped 40%
- AEC dropped 30%[115]

The drop in these identifies that EMF causes a stress-like response, and a low oxygen environment. Results like these help explain the fatigue people are experiencing while working with EMF devices. Since many with unexplained fatigue are being diagnosed with chronic fatigue syndrome, it is important to look at their EMF exposure as a probable cause. It is also important to recognize that a body that does not have its full supply of energy is subject to deteriorating into many debilitating conditions.

Food Allergies

EMF – Affect on Food Allergies
There has not been much connection of food allergies as being the result of EMF radiation, however, the number of people stating they developed food allergies for the first time has increased dramatically, especially since smart meters have been deployed throughout cities in the United States and around the world.

Leaky gut syndrome occurs due to the tight junction cells of the intestines being compromised by exposure to electromagnetic radiation. This is the same leaking that occurs in the blood-brain barrier as discussed earlier in this book. The leaking in the gut results in food particles entering the blood stream that generate reactions when the body creates antibodies to the foreign substances, which then circulate in the body. When this happens, people experience allergic reactions to the food they eat. Since the radiations are now constant, especially where smart meters are installed, there has to be a continual healing regimen implemented to repair these holes in the intestinal lining. Healing the gut results in a lessening of the food allergy reactions.

I myself became extremely allergic to almost every food within a month of the electrical smart meters being installed in my neighborhood. I knew I had many antibodies to foods due to mercury poisoning 13 years earlier. At that time, once I spent 2 years healing my leaky gut, I could eat again. After the smart meter installations, I had constant hives from no matter what I ate. I gave up eating and experienced a rapid weight loss. When I started taking a product that helped my pituitary make and release my own human growth hormone (HGH), within several weeks my allergic responses disappeared, and I could eat most everything again.

The cells of the entire digestive lining require human growth hormone (HGH) to develop correctly and to maintain the intestinal lining integrity. Providing the cells with this essential building block they need to rebuild from the constant EMF assault can assist in restoring the integrity of the GI tract barrier. Relief can be very quick because the entire gut lining turns over every 48 to 72 hours. I rapidly regained my lost weight plus more, as it was such a pleasure to be able to eat again without having hives within hours of eating.

Autoimmune Diseases
Leaky gut also results in autoimmune diseases, as the body recognizes the food particles as foreign and creates antibodies that can attack the body's own tissues, rather than protect the body from invasion—the purpose they were designed for.

> **Warning**
>
> Potential Health Effects – impact on intestinal lining creating leaky gut:
>
> Autoimmune diseases
> Hashimoto's disease

Memory

EMF – Affect on Short-term Memory / Alzheimer's

Hippocampus Cell Loss

One important type of cell that makes up the hippocampus (area of the brain responsible for storing and retrieving memo-

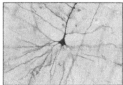

Pyramidal cell

ries) is called a pyramidal cell. When rats were exposed to the EMF frequency of 835 MHz for different exposure times and absorption rates 1 hour a day for 1 month, there was an almost complete loss of pyramidal cells in areas within the hippocampus. In this same study, the researchers also identified changes in cellular calcium levels, which they warned could have harmful effects on the normal functions of the hippocampus involved in nerve cell communication.[116]

In one study, rats were exposed to 900 MHz cell phone radiation during their whole prenatal pregnancy period and then additionally for another 80 days after they were born. The phone was in talking mode for 30 minutes a day, while the rest of the day it was in standby mode, making the level of exposure far lower than the average phone user today. The rat brains exposed to this level of radiation showed a 50% decrease in the number of pyramidal nerve cells. They also identified that 73% of the cells in the cortex of the brain experienced a reduction in blood flow. These findings led the researchers to state:

"In conclusion, MF (900 MHz) affected some biochemical parameters, especially the cortex region of the brain [outer layer involved with muscle movement, sensation, memory, thought, and reasoning]."[117]

Loss of these critically important cells identifies why some people report problems with memory as well as mental confusion (brain fog) after EMF radiation exposure.

Warning

Potential Health Effects – hippocampus cell loss:

Memory loss

Nosebleeds

EMF – Affect on Nosebleeds / Bleeding Under Skin

EMF Oxidation Damage to Blood Vessels
Research also shows that the blood vessels are undergoing damage from oxidation stress. Based on changes in the blood of rabbits exposed to 900 MHz GSM (Global System for Mobile communication) at a SAR of 0.02 mW/cm2 for 30 minutes a day for 7 days, researchers state their results suggest that EMR induces an oxidative stress within the blood vessels of rabbits.[118]

The oxidation damage to the blood vessels combined with decreased numbers of platelets (See EMF – Affect on White Blood Cells, and Platelets) may also be why people are experiencing frequent nosebleeds. This could also help correlate why people are experiencing bleeding under their skin, and doctors are unable to tell them why. I see it in many people, and this happened to me when I was using computers and cell phones, before I found solutions that strengthen the body's energy field, making it less vulnerable to EMF radiation.

EMF – Affect on Blood Clots
Endothelial cells are smooth cells that line the blood vessels and the heart that can secrete substances that either aid in clot formation, or reduce the possibility of clot formations. Researchers exposed an endothelial cell line to electromagnetic radiation with and without the radiation protection provided by a Faraday cage, which is an enclosure that is designed to block EMF. They determined that the environmental electromagnetic field significantly increases the risk of blood clots.[119]

EMF – Connection to Stroke

There are 2 types of strokes. Ischemic strokes occur when a blood clot or fat deposit blocks an artery supplying blood to the brain, which accounts for 80% of strokes. Hemorrhagic strokes, which account for the remaining 20%, occur where an artery bursts due to weakness in the artery wall.[120]

EMF, by creating changes in the red blood cell membrane causing them to stick together, as well as causing damage to the endothelium cells that line blood vessels, can lead to an increased risk for blood clots to form. This combined with oxidation damage to the inside of blood vessels identifies that EMF radiation could be why there has been an increase in strokes, especially occurring at younger ages. In 2012, a United States study identified that strokes under age 55 increased in a little over 10 years from 12.9% in 1993 – 1994 to 18.6% in 2005. The researchers stated: "This is of great public health significance because strokes in younger patients carry the potential for greater lifetime burden of disability and because some potential contributors identified for this trend are modifiable."[121]

This trend has also been identified in England. The Stroke Association in England reported a rise in strokes in younger men aged 40 – 54. The number rose dramatically in just 14 years, as there were 4,260 hospital admissions in the year 2000 compared to 6,221 in 2014.[122]

EMF radiation needs to be recognized as a possible cause of this increase in strokes since oxidation damage inside blood vessel walls, combined with red blood cells sticking together in rouleaux, could be contributing factors in this increase found in younger people.

Itchy Skin / Rashes

EMF – Affect on Itching / Tingling / Burning Skin / Rashes

As a result of the holes in cellular membranes created by EMF radiation, the calcium concentration within and outside the cell becomes unbalanced. Without the normal calcium gradient, skin cells do not develop through their normal differentiation cycle and cannot perform their normal barrier protection by developing into keratinocytes—the tough dead outer layer of our skin.[123]

Additionally, research has revealed that when the pesticide atrazine is combined with EMF radiation of 50 Hz for 4 hours a day in young rats from day 23 to day 53 there is a degranulation of mast cells in the skin. The opened granules release their contents of histamine, serotonin, and heparin. The histamine creates the itching and the anticoagulant heparin creates the bleeding that many are experiencing on exposure to cell phones, computers, TVs, and smart meters. Below is a picture of mast cells with their many granules that are throughout their cells.[124]

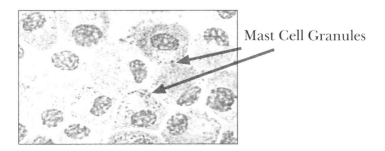

Mast Cells with their histamine and heparin granules.

Sadly, the itching rash reaction from the histamine, termed *screen dermatitis*, has been recognized since 1994, yet the medical field still diagnoses it as scabies. See more detail regarding changes in the skin in EHS people compared to others who do not experience the itching in Chapter 10: Major Organ Damage – Heart, Kidney, Bladder, Skin.

EMF – Affect on Numbness in Hands or Feet
Many people are reporting that they are experiencing burning, numbness, and tingling of their hands and up their arms when holding their cell phones in their hands, or down their legs when their cell phones are in their pocket. One article stated that the identification of burning in response to the frequencies that cell phones radiate include induced hyperthermia in one patient who was exposed to 915 MHz microwave radiation. They reported the patient had such a severe "burning" sensation in the arm at the lowest measurable power from the generator that further treatment was discontinued.[125]

One study cited that there were case reports of peripheral neurological effects of radio frequency radiation that describe mainly disturbances of dysaesthesia (impairment of sensation). Reports have come after exposure to the frequency ranges from low MHz to higher GHz. Some symptoms are temporary and others are lasting. They identified that very high intensity exposures may cause gross injury to nerves cells. In a small percentage of people, lower intensity exposures like those from cell phones cause the dysaesthesia, yet when investigating this with ordinary nerve conduction studies they show no abnormalities. This means our present measuring techniques are not sensitive enough to detect the changes that EMF radiation creates at the cellular level. The researchers stated: "It is concluded that RFR [radio frequency radiation] from mobile phones can cause peripheral neurophysiological changes in some persons. The effects occur at exposure levels below the present safety levels for RFR."[126]

It has been difficult to identify studies that examine mobile phone use with the feeling of numbness, burning, and tingling that many people are expressing they feel when using their phone. A simple Internet search finds many people attempting to find answers for their symptoms of their hand going numb while using a cell phone. Studies show that nerve cells undergo oxidation damage, as well as are proven to be killed on exposure to cell phone frequencies. It may be that nerve cell damage leads to the numb feeling. In the future, studies will emerge and provide biochemical explanations, but for now be aware that this is a frequent complaint, particularly with the more powerful 3G and 4G cell phones. Especially the 4G, as many are stating they cannot hold them without tingling, burning, and numbness.

Demyelination of the nerve cells may be one explanation for these symptoms, as well as helps explain why some people experience EHS, while others do not. The myelin sheath on nerve cells provides the electrical insulation for the nervous system. It develops rapidly throughout the first years of life, and is vital for a healthy, functioning nervous system. Scientists reviewing the studies published regarding the affect on myelin found radio-frequency electromagnetic fields (RF–EMFs) are associated with:

1. Significant lesions in the myelin sheath of rats
2. A greater risk of multiple sclerosis in a subgroup
3. Changes in proteins related to myelin production
4. Physical and demyelination symptoms in EHS people

The researchers stated the evidence indicated there is an association between RF–EMF exposure and either myelin deterioration or a direct impact on nerve conduction. Identifying that this may account for many electrohypersensitivity symptoms, they also warn the most vulnerable to these damaging changes are:

1. The fetus in the uterus
2. Children through the mid-teen years
3. The ill
4. The elderly[127]

Demyelination is connected to many disabling disorders, including multiple sclerosis. For more detail on Multiple Sclerosis see Chapter 7: Alzheimer's Disease / CNS / MS.

Involuntary Muscle Contractions

EMF – Affect on Involuntary Muscle Contractions

In the Maine smart meter survey, 25% of the people responded that they experienced involuntary muscle contractions after exposure to the smart meters on their homes. Studying involuntary movements of hands of people riding in a moving car, researchers identified that radiofrequency radiation created the movement that correlated to the intensity of the measured 100 MHz electromagnetic field that was emanating from a tower approximately 18 miles (30 km) away. They stated: "In conclusion, RF irradiation seems to affect the human hand reflexes of sensitive persons in a moving van along a normal public road which may have significance in traffic safety."[128]

Testing human sensitivity to FM and TV antennas, researchers exposed 29 adults of different ages to intermittent radiation by using a moving shield to block the electromagnetic radiation. There were 9 of the 29 who experienced involuntary hand movement when the shield was not blocking the radiation. The researchers concluded that sensitive persons seem to react to crossing through stationary waves of the FM-radio or TV broad-casting signals.[129] This study identified that approximately 30% of people are affected by involuntary muscle contractions upon exposure to electromagnetic radiation, which approximates the 25% seen in the respondents to the Maine smart meter survey who stated they experienced muscle contractions.

Lyme Disease

EMF – Lyme Disease or EHS?

The numbers of people being diagnosed with Lyme disease for their many and varied physical symptoms have been rapidly increasing in the 21st century, so much so that medical conferences are including sessions on Lyme disease. The name for the disease arose from Lyme, Connecticut when in the mid-1970s the people living in the community were experiencing many unexplainable symptoms. In 1975, the Connecticut State Health Department reported approximately 60 children and adults were experiencing similar symptoms, or about 4.3 per 1,000 residents.[130] At the time, they theorized that due to the skin rashes it was being caused by a virus that was transmitted through insect bites. In 1982, Dr. Willy Burgdorfer identified an organism carried by ticks and identified it as the spirochete *Borrelia burgdorferi*.

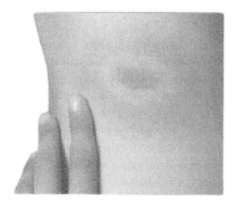

Bull's Eye Rash from Deer Tick

Lyme Disease Symptoms

Rashes anywhere on the body.

Fatigue / tiredness

Chest pain / heart palpitations / pulse skip

Headache / shortness of breath

Joint / muscle pain / stiffness of the joints / neck / back

Tingling / numbness / burning / stabbing sensations

Increased motion sickness / nausea / vomiting

Light-headedness / dizziness / poor balance / wooziness / difficulty walking

Difficulty in thinking / concentration / reading / confusion

Forgetfulness / poor short term memory / disorientation / getting lost

Double / blurry vision / eye pain

Buzzing / ringing in ears / ear pain

Seizure activity / tremor

Mood swings / violent outbursts / irritability / depression / panic anxiety attack

Disturbed sleep (too much or too little, early awakening) / insomnia

Testicular / pelvic pain / irregular menses / sexual dysfunction / loss of libido

Bull's eye rash at bite site

Source: Lyme Disease Association website. Lyme Disease Symptoms. Retrieved September 30, 2014 from: www.lymediseaseassociation.org/images/NewDirectory/ Resources/Printables/SymptomList_2013.pdf

These symptoms are identical to what are described throughout this chapter and the remainder of this book, with the explanations of how they can arise due to EMF radiation exposure. These symptoms also arise due to the radiation that is emitted by communication towers. Surveying inhabitants of a town acquiring its first cell phone tower, they found 23.5% experienced headaches, 28.2% memory changes, 18.8% dizziness, 9.4% tremors, 21.7% depressive symptoms, and 23.5% sleep disturbances; all of which were significantly higher among exposed inhabitants compared to the controls who were not exposed to the cell

tower.[131] These symptoms are critically important to pay attention to, especially since the number of cell towers has grown ex-
ponentially in the U.S., climbing from 900 in 1985 to 205,000 in
2015.

When comparing the list of Lyme symptoms with those of
electromagnetic hypersensitivity sickness (EHS), the only difference is the absence of the bull's eye rash in EHS. Of those diagnosed with Lyme, less than half experienced the bull's eye rash
and many do not recall having had a tick bite.

The lack of recognition of symptoms arising due to EMF exposure could be why many are being treated for Lyme disease
today and undergo a continuing series of antibiotic treatments
for years, yet continue suffering the same debilitating symptoms.
The present theory for why the antibiotics are not helping these
patients is that they were not diagnosed when they first infected,
so they could be treated early enough for the antibiotics to work.

Laboratory Testing

Lyme testing requires positive results confirmation from two
different types of laboratory tests, each designed to detect the
antibodies that are created upon exposure to the spirochete.
Being a Clinical Laboratory Scientist, I know laboratory tests
have a certain degree of inaccuracy. This is particularly true for
Lyme disease testing, even being called "unreliable" by a Lyme
disease research website. Different results are found on the
same specimens when they are sent to different laboratories, and
are positive in only between 20% to 70% in those who still have
symptoms after antibiotic treatment.[132]

Summary

Since so many are being diagnosed today with Lyme disease,
it could be that either both syndromes are occurring at the same
time, or there are EHS individuals being misdiagnosed who are
really experiencing electromagnetic sensitivity. This helps explain why laboratory tests are negative and the repeated courses
of antibiotics do not bring relief as antibiotics will not reduce
EHS symptoms. For them, reducing EMF exposure would be

a very small investment to determine whether some, or all, of the symptoms are the result of EMF radiation. If they are, it is possible to obtain relief from the symptoms by taking steps to reduce exposure and mitigate EMF radiation, which are much less invasive on the body's immune system compared to the repeated courses of antibiotics recommended for Lyme treatment. Since electromagnetic radiations are cumulative, it could be only matter of time before many start feeling one or more of the symptoms described in this chapter and throughout the book that may be being misdiagnosed as Lyme disease.

Exciting News:
EHS Symptoms Have Been Validated

Proof regarding electromagnetic hypersensitivity was published December 2015 in *Reviews on Environmental Health* on the work of scientists who have been studying 700 electromagnetic sensitive, as well as multiple chemically sensitive people, since 2009. They found that chronic inflammation was the key process for the development of these conditions. The EHS people showed increased histamine, blood-brain barrier leakage markers, anti-myelin antibodies, decreased melatonin, and oxidative stress. In addition, using cerebral ultrasounds they found inflammation of the limbic system. All of these indicators suggest a risk of chronic neurodegenerative disease. In studying animals, the researchers found similar changes in these biomarkers.[133]

The studies throughout this book document that all of these changes can occur with electromagnetic radiation exposure. Identifying these changes shows the symptoms EHS people feel are biochemical alterations that can occur upon exposure to electromagnetic radiation. The individual variability of symptoms makes it difficult for those who do not have symptoms to identify with or accept what electrosensitive people are feeling. The facts are clear, it is time to recognize the canaries in our world that are feeling EHS symptoms are making the clarion call that EMF radiation is harming each of us, and it is only a matter of time before others feel the symptoms. Let us heed their cries of warnings.

Chapter 6

The Brain

EMF – Affect on the Brain

Current studies reveal that so many areas of the brain are showing damage from EMF radiations, the following is an overview of the functions of the various parts of the brain that are revealing cell deterioration, or death upon exposure to EMF. This background will help in understanding the importance of each study's findings.

**Parts of the Brain
Scientists Have Identified
As Being Damaged by EMF Radiation**

Cortex
(Processing information; language)

Temporal lobe
(Auditory / visual perception,
memory, speech, and
emotional response)

Hypothalamus
(Hormones; automatic
functions)

Thalamus
(Sensory perception
and movement)

Frontal cortex
(Planning)

Striatum
(Motivation with body
movement and inhibition)

Amygdala
(Basic emotions)

Cerebellum
(Coordinate
movement)

Caudate putamen
(Controls motor movement
and learning)

Brain stem
(Basic body
movements)

Hippocampus
(Learning and storing
memories)

The Limbic System

A group of brain structures comprised of the: amygdala, hippocampus, regions of the limbic cortex, and the septal area that surrounds the brain stem and forms connections with the hypothalamus, thalamus, and cerebral cortex. It is a set of evolutionarily primitive brain structures that are located on top of the brainstem and buried under the cortex. Its functions include the sense of smell, behavior, learning, long-term memory, emotions, and drives.

Amygdala

The amygdala is responsible for emotional processing, including pleasure, fear and anger, as well as where the tendency to develop a negative attitude towards the environment originates. It connects with the hippocampus to form memories, which is why emotional events are remembered more than mild occurrences. One of the primary outcomes of damage is seizures. Abnormal electrical activity causes it to become inappropriately hyperactive, leading people to sudden attacks of rage and even to becoming violent.

Brain Stem

The brain stem connects the spinal cord with the cerebellum and is where all information to and from our body passes through on the way to or from the brain. It controls our autonomic functions that we do not have to consciously think about, such as heart rate; blood pressure; breathing; and digestion. It plays a crucial role in our basic attention, arousal, and our consciousness.

Cerebellum

The cerebellum controls motor movement coordination, balance, equilibrium and muscle tone. It contains the hundreds of millions of nerve cells that are necessary for processing data information between body muscles and the nerve cells that are involved in motor control. As such, it is essential for our fine movement coordination, as well as balance and equilibrium. One of the major symptoms of electromagnetic sensitivity is vertigo and dizziness that arises with loss of equilibrium. Death of this area of the brain from EMF may be one of the reasons for the marked dizziness some people feel.

Caudate Putamen
The caudate putamen is a large structure within the brain that is involved in a very complex feedback loop to prepare and assist in movement of the arms and legs.

Cortex of brain
The cortex is the outer layer of the brain. So when talking about the frontal cortex, it is describing the outer layer of the frontal lobe.

Frontal Cortex
The frontal lobes of the cortex not only are involved in conscious muscle movement, they provide the ability to think things through and determine how to use information from other parts of the brain. Our personality arises from the frontal lobes, as they furnish us with the ability to reason, make choices and judgments, solve problems and take action, as well as control the present living environment and plan for the future. This part of the brain accumulates the memories that remind us how to communicate, and to control our emotions allowing us to interact properly in social or public situations. It also provides the empathy that allows us to understand the thinking and experiences of others.

Hippocampus
The hippocampus is responsible for the ability to store and retrieve memories. Damage to this structure results in difficulties with memories, or complete inability to store and recall information, which is important for learning new things. It is also important for a person's ability to overcome fear responses. In addition, research has shown that it shrinks in size due to chronic stress.

Striatum
Functionally, the striatum assists in coordinating the motivation of body movements, controlling fine-motor functions, and providing the ability to inhibit behavior in social interactions.[134] Atrophy of the striatum is seen in Parkinson's, as well as Huntington's disease.

Temporal Lobe
The temporal lobe's primary function is the processing and analyzing auditory information. It also is involved in memory, emotions and behavior, and speech.

EMF – Cell Death in the Brain

In an article published in *Brain Research* in 1981, U.S. Navy personnel determined that the rat brain exposed to pulsing 2.8 GHz (2800 MHz) radiation for 60 minutes had increased blood flow to all 17 regions of the brain they examined, which included the pituitary, pineal gland, hypothalamus, and cerebellum.[135] This indicates the radiation has a global effect on the brain.

To determine whether brain damage has occurred, researchers look at an increase in glial cells that replace brain nerve cells that have died. Glial cells are important in that they are the most abundant cell types in the central nervous system and include oligodendrocytes, astrocytes, ependymal cells, Schwann cells, microglia, and satellite cells. These cells play active roles in the brain surrounding, supporting, and insulating the important nerve cells. Astrocytes are glial cells that provide maintenance of the blood-brain barrier as well. Astrocytosis (or astrogliosis) is the inflammation of the astrocytes. It is an abnormal increase in their numbers and their processes due to the destruction of nearby neurons from multiple different causes including trauma or lack of oxygen.[136] (Cell phone use results in decreased oxygen in the tissues.) The trauma result in scars in the central nervous system that involve the production of a dense fibrous network of astrocytes. Creating scaring, these abnormal cells replace the normal nerve cells that have died. This central nervous system damage is seen in many diseases including multiple sclerosis and stroke, where neurons die, disappear, and are replaced with the fibrous reactive astrocytosis cells.[137] To evaluate the amount of reactive astrocytosis, investigators utilize the glial fibrillary acidic protein (GFAP) expression in rat brains, which is a measure of the amount of scaring that has occurred.[138]

Measuring GFAP expression to determine the effects of mobile phone on the nervous system, researchers exposed rats for 45 minutes a day to a GSM mobile phone radiation of 900 MHz at SAR 1.5 W/kg (close to the U.S. FCC 1.6 W/kg allowable SAR). They also exposed a group to 15 minutes a day at a SAR = 6 W/kg. Both groups were exposed for 5 days a week for 8 weeks. They found after 3 and 10 days exposure the GFAP expression increased, identifying fibrous astrocytosis network replacing dead nerve cells in the brain's prefrontal cortex, cerebellar cortex, hippocampus, striatum, and the caudate putamen. This occurred from both the 1.5 and the 6 W/kg SAR. Their results led the researchers to conclude that exposure to 900 MHz EMF signal for 2 months could adversely affect the brain, resulting in fibrous (scared) cells rather than active nerve cells. The researchers concluded: "Our study and previous works link GSM exposure to astrogliosis that can lead to neuronal damage, including cell death, synapse [nerve cell junction] loss, axonal [transmitting fiber] damage, and myelin damage."[139]

All this is describing damage to nerve cells, loss of their ability to communicate with other nerve cells, and their death. This study also identifies that EMF radiation creates the kind of damage to the brain that is seen in strokes, described earlier in this book as occurring in increasing numbers in younger aged people. This study raises concern as it reveals damage to the brain cells at a power level below the maximum 1.6 W/kg SAR that is currently regarded as safe for human exposure by the Federal Communications Commission (FCC) in the United States.

Brain Damage

Researchers in order to determine the structural changes of electromagnetic radiation (EMR) waves in the brain's frontal cortex, brain stem and cerebellum, subjected the heads of adult male rats to 900, 1800, and 2450 MHz microwave irradiation for 1 hour a day for 2 months. The brain cells after exposure to the EMR were found to have shrunken in their cytoplasm (gel-like body of the cell between the membrane and nucleus) and the DNA within the nucleus was condensed, which is known to be irreversible. They also showed decreased antioxidant capacity, which indicates that oxidation from the EMR required the cell to use its supply of antioxidants. In addition, there was an increase in the Oxidative Stress Index, which means a lessening of the body's ability to detoxify. These observations led the investigators to state that EMR causes structural changes in the areas they examined: frontal cortex, brain stem and cerebellum, creating a deterioration that could lead to disease, including both loss of brain function in these areas, and to the development of cancer.[140]

In looking at the potential of cell phones to affect brain nerve cells, a 2006 study that analyzed blood flow in the brain exposed to cell phone radiation found there was a decrease in blood flow in the area beneath the antenna, while at the same time there was an increase in blood flow in the front of the brain. The researchers concluded that their results are consistent with the emerging evidence that EMF radiation induces changes in nerve cell activity.[141]

This was confirmed in a 2009 study when investigators who exposed human volunteers to mobile phones identified that the 900 MHz GSM frequency appears to act on the brain's electrical activity.[142]

Researchers in 2013 found the same results working with marine mollusk neurons, which are nerve cells that send information long distances to other cells. The researchers concluded that EMF radiation damages the ability of neurons to store information, decreasing their memory capacity, and preventing them from performing their vital role of transmitting information to other parts of the body.[143] This could result in problems with motor coordination.

Investigators analyzing rats exposed to 2.45 GHz (2450 MHz) for 2 hours a day for 45 days identified a significant decrease in melatonin, and significant increases in both an enzyme and a protein that can cause brain damage, as well as an increase in calcium. Identifying significant changes to such important chemicals led the researchers to state:

> ". . . [these changes] may cause significant damage in the brain due to chronic exposure of these radiations. These biomarkers clearly indicate possible health implications of such exposures."[144]

Metabolism Changes
Studies reveal that EMF radiations affect blood glucose (sugar) metabolism. In measuring human volunteers exposed to cell phone radiation on their heads, they found that:

> ". . . 50-minute cell phone exposure was associated with increased brain glucose metabolism in the region closest to the antenna."[145]

Other researchers, using a PET scan (positron emission to-mography) to track the effects of 33 minutes of exposure from a *pulse* modulated 902.4 MHz Global System cell phone frequency, found reduced glucose metabolism in the area of the brain underneath the cell phone. They concluded:

"Our results show that short-term mobile phone exposure can locally suppress brain energy metabolism in humans."[146]

These results are conflicting because they show both an increase and decrease in metabolism, however they highlight that EMF radiation affects how cells utilize glucose. This becomes an important consideration because glucose (sugar) is the only fuel the brain uses for energy. Altering glucose metabolism would necessarily alter brain functioning. Any changes in the brain have the potential to impact our behaviors and our lives.

Warning

Potential Health Effects – altered brain glucose metabolism. Any condition arising from changes in brain sugar (glucose):

Irritability
Aggression
Mental confusion

Chapter 7

Alzheimer's Disease / CNS / MS

EMF – Connection to Alzheimer's Disease

To review the information contained in EMF – Affect on the Brain: the hippocampus is the part of the brain that is involved in episodic memories. This type of memory allows people to recall events, whether they are major or minor, that they have personally experienced. It provides the ability to remember in time sequence the places and times and the emotions associated with the event. The more emotionally charged,

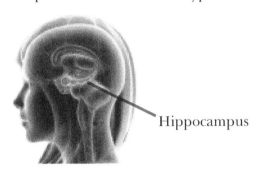

Hippocampus

the more we remember. Providing the ability to permanently consolidate the events, it creates awareness of one's identity and existence in time. This includes the ability to process current events and remember new locations and routes.[147]

The first area of the brain that appears to show damage in Alzheimer's patient is the hippocampus, which is associated with the episodic memory decline and disorientation that Alzheimer's patients experience. EMF radiation becomes suspect as a potential cause of Alzheimer's when multiple studies identify that cell phone radiation can damage the hippocampus.

In a 2008 article published in *Brain Research*, scientists exposing pregnant rats to an EMF of 900 MHz for 60 minutes a day throughout gestation found there were decreased cells in the hippocampus of the offspring.[148] Again in 2009, the researchers further identified cell phone hippocampal cell loss, which is discussed in EMF – Impact on the Teenage Brain.

In Alzheimer's disease (AD), amyloid plaques are surrounded by reactive astrocytes with an increased expression of intermediate filaments including glial fibrillary acidic protein (GFAP). The number of astrocytes increase during the development of AD.[149] Previously in the section on the brain, the formation of astrocytes and GFAP were identified as being created by cell phone radiation.

Further confirmation that EMF radiations, like those created by cell phones, may be one of the reasons for the increasing incidence in Alzheimer's is found in a study published in 2008 by Drs. Henrietta Nittby, Gustav Grafstrom, and D.P. Tian. Exposing rats to the cell phone frequency of 900 MHz, they found that the rats had impaired short-term memory, which was identified by difficulty in remembering objects and their order of presentation.[150]

The 2015 study in the section on EMF – Affect on the Blood-brain Barrier that confirmed the leakage of the blood-brain barrier from EMF, also identified that there was loss of spatial memory (the ability to remember locations of objects) in the rats exposed for 28 days to the standard cell phone frequency of 900 MHz for 3 hours a day.[151]

Based on results like these, future exploration should look at the role EMF may play in AD pathology.

Warning

Potential Health Effects – on the hippocampus:

Alzheimer's disease

As stated earlier, 900 MHz radiation decreases GABA producing Purkinje cells in the cerebellum. Scientists have identified decreased GABA functioning results in the loss of episodic memory, and associate it with dysfunction of the hippocampus.[152] Alzheimer's connection to decreased GABA functioning is confirmed as a factor in a 2013 article published in *Neurological Science*. In analyzing patients' brains, researchers found that those with Alzheimer's had significantly decreased GABA (33% less) when compared to controls.[153]

Warning

Potential Health Effects – chronic EMF exposure on the hippocampus:

Decreased GABA function
Loss of episodic memory
Alzheimer's disease

EMF – Environmental Exposures

The biochemistry of this effect does suggest that lifestyles with more EMF exposure could increase the risk of developing Alzheimer's disease. Studies looking into potential risk factors do reveal that this is the case. One study looking at in-patients in a hospital compared to matched controls found 3 things that correlated with an increased risk of Alzheimer's. They were:

1. Negative life events
2. Family history of dementia
3. Early exposure to magnetic fields.[154]

In another study, people over age 70 were screened for cognitive impairment. They found that those people who had electromagnetic field radiation exposure at work had a significantly increased incidence of Alzheimer's disease compared to a control group. Those who had electric heating in their homes also had a significant increase in incidence.[155]

An additional study looking at risks for Alzheimer's also found a significantly increased incidence of Alzheimer's in people who had occupations with likely exposure to electromagnetic fields, which led the researchers to conclude:

"These results are consistent with previous findings regarding the hypothesis that electromagnetic field exposure is etiologically [the cause] associated with the occurrence of Alzheimer's disease."[156]

EMF – Connection to Parkinson's / Lou Gehrig's Disease

A study published in the *Archives of Environmental Health* identified evidence that occupations associated with electrical exposure lead to an increased risk of not only the neurodegenerative disease of Alzheimer's, but also Parkinson's disease, as well as Lou Gehrig's Disease (Amyotrophic lateral sclerosis – ALS). The case-control study looked at U.S. male death certificates containing occupational codes to compare occupations with electrical exposure to controls that were matched for age and calendar time.

U.S. Male Deaths:
Electrical and Non-Electrical Occupations

	Odds ratio
Alzheimer's disease	1.2
Parkinson's disease	1.1
ALS (amyotrophic lateral sclerosis)	1.3 – 5.0

These results indicate that there is an increased risk of these diseases of 10%, 20%, 30%, and more found in workers exposed to electricity. The largest associations with all 3 diseases were found in power plant operators.[157]

Warning

Potential Health Effects – electrical exposure:

Alzheimer's disease
Parkinson's disease
Lou Gehrig's disease

 The EMF exposure causing damage to the hippocampus, as well as the cerebellum, supports investigating an EMF connection to the increased incidence that is being seen in Alzheimer's disease. This is critically important as everyone deserves to have the ability to enjoy their golden years.

EMF – Affect on the Spinal Cord

Research has identified that the spinal cord acts as a natural antenna, with electric voltage and current distribution dependent on the frequency that it is exposed to. In testing the frequencies between 100 to 2400 MHz (2.4 GHz), researchers found that the FM radio range around 100 MHz creates a peak voltage and current response with significant strength to potentially cause changes in the central nervous system (CNS). This helped them identify the mechanism behind EMF energy leakage into the CNS, and the possible contribution of the CNS energy leakage towards the weakening of the blood-brain barrier (BBB). These investigators concluded that:

"This work can contribute to the understanding of the mechanism behind EMF energy leakage into the CNS, and the possible contribution of the latter energy leakage towards the weakening of the blood-brain barrier (BBB), whose degradation is associated with the progress of many diseases, including acquired immunodeficiency syndrome (AIDS)."[158]

Other researchers have also established that cell phone use causes leakage between the blood and cerebrospinal fluid (CSF). They identified an increase of a thyroid hormone carrier, transthyretin (TTR), in the blood, which is indicative of spinal cord leakage. Time since first use for both cell phones and cordless phones was associated with significantly higher TTR regardless of the amount of use. With short-term use, women showed higher levels the sooner the blood was drawn after a phone call.[159] This increased leakage identified in women is worth further investigating, since there are several conditions, including Alzheimer's disease and MS that affect a greater proportion of women compared to men.

Warning
Potential Health Effects – leakage of the spinal cord and blood-brain barrier:

Alzheimer's	Brain tumors
AIDS	MS
Brain infections	Neurological diseases

EMF – Affect on Multiple Sclerosis

Investigations into spinal cord leakage also help identify why more women are impacted by autoimmune diseases like multiple sclerosis (MS). Statistics are revealing there has been a significant increase in the ratio of women to men. In 1940, women with MS out numbered men by 2 to 1; a ratio that doubled to 4 to 1 by the year 2000.[160]

Reasons to Suspect Cell Phone Radiation Connection to MS

Disruption of the BBB is one of the earliest abnormalities that is seen in brains of those with MS. It is accompanied by increases in inflammatory substances. These investigations are revealing that there is a connection between problems with the blood-brain barrier and MS.

In 2006, researchers reviewed the evidence that MS is associated with a problem with the integrity of the cells that form the blood-brain barrier. They identified there has been little investigation in regards to whether these cellular abnormalities could play a crucial role in the formation of the MS lesions, as well as in the progression of the disease.[161]

As detailed in Chapter 4, EMF – Affect on the Blood-brain Barrier, there are multiple studies that have identified that EMF radiation from cell phones results in disruption of tight junction cells. They also create leaks in the blood-brain barrier. Both of these conditions are found in those with MS.[162]

Cell phone radiation is also identified as causing damage to endothelial cells. Much research supports endothelial cell "stress" and cell death as a hallmark characteristic of MS.[163] Yet, another link to EMF radiation.

As described earlier, the radiation can cause nerve cell demyelination. Since MS symptoms arise out of demyelination of the nerve cells, EMF are also suspect.

Blood-brain Barrier

Smooth muscle cells   Endothelial cells

Brain

Tight junction cells

Blood

In view of the facts that the evidence clearly reveals that EMF disrupt tight junction cells and the blood-brain barrier, cause endothelial cell stress, and demyelinate nerve cells, investigating EMF effects are essential in working towards avenues that will assist those suffering from the debilitating symptoms of MS.

Warning

Potential Health Effects:

    MS development and exacerbation

Mercury Amalgams

It is possible that some of the symptoms that people feel with cell phone use are due to the effects of mercury being released from any mercury amalgams they may have in their mouth while being on a cell phone. Amalgams are the fillings that look silver, but are 50% mercury. Researchers investigating this measured the amount of mercury release in people who had mercury amalgam fillings in their teeth upon exposure to cell phone use and to MRI (magnetic resonance imaging). They stated:

> "Lack of ionizing radiation and the low energy level emitted from cell phones has led to the public perception that mobile phone use is safe. The results obtained in this study show a significant increase of the mercury release in urine after mobile phone use."

> "In this study, it was shown that MRI and microwave radiation emitted from mobile phones significantly increased the release of mercury from dental amalgam restorations."

This means that cell phone use may cause health problems for people who have silver mercury amalgam fillings in their teeth. The researchers felt primary concern is for small children, pregnant women, elderly, and people who are sensitive to mercury, which includes those who genetically are less able to release mercury from their body (genetically they have apolipoprotein E-4 [ApoE-4]).[164]

The apolipoprotein-E (apo-E) genotype has been identified as an indicator of susceptibility to heavy metals like lead and mercury, which cause nerve damage. The apo-E-4 is a major risk factor for neurodegenerative conditions, including Alzheimer's disease (AD), and MS.[165] People who have the APO-E2 and APO-E3 can process mercury out of the brain, but individuals that only have APO-E4 have mercury poisoning symptoms as they cannot transport mercury out of the brain.[166]

Researchers exploring the connection that mercury from amalgam may be related to multiple sclerosis (MS), found MS subjects to have significantly lower levels of red blood cells and hemoglobin, lower levels of lymphocytes (white blood cells), and significantly higher levels of hair mercury compared to MS subjects with amalgam removal. The MS subjects with amalgams had significantly more (33.7%) flare ups or relapses over a year compared to the MS volunteers with amalgam removal.[167]

From the evidence provided earlier in this book, all of these can be created by cell phone radiations. Hearing loss, Alzheimer's, kidney damage, and MS have been connected to the presence of amalgam fillings.[168] The association of mercury release from cell phone use and mercury toxicity related to these, as well as other conditions, is well worth investigating.

The problem with holding the phone near the side of your mouth is that the energy from the device has the potential to heat the fillings. Mercury amalgam can vaporize at temperatures not far from body temperature. Researchers need to determine whether the people who express they have symptoms on exposure to EMF have move silver mercury amalgam fillings in their teeth, compared to those who do not experience symptoms.

Multiple Sclerosis (MS) Increasing in Sardinia, Italy

The connection of cell phone use to MS is important to consider. MS rates are increasing around the world. Due to Sardinia, Italy having one of the highest risks for multiple sclerosis worldwide with prevalence rates of 150 per 100,000 residents, researchers looked at the differences in incidence rates between 1965 and 1999 in the Sardinia province of Sassari.

The mean annual incidence rate increased significantly from 1.1 per 100,000 in 1965-1969 to 5.8 in 1995-1999. They state that this marked increase of MS incidence points to a corresponding change in environmental risk factors.[169]

Four years later, the researchers identified that the incidence was increasing significantly in older aged people and in females. They still identified that the increases are the result of recent lifestyle changes (environmental), which may be combined with a highly susceptible genetic background.[170]

MS Increasing in Norway

Research in Norway is identifying that MS has increased 10-fold over the last 50 years. The number of females versus males has also increased. They also identified that second-generation immigrants have an increased risk of MS compared to the populations that remained in their countries of origin. The investigators concluded that their findings indicate that environmental risk factors are responsible for the increase. Additionally they stated early adolescence appears as a time of increased susceptibility. Bringing awareness to the importance of the vitamin D deficiency that is pandemic today in the world, they also identified that taking a vitamin D supplement might reduce the risk of developing MS.[171]

With MS increasing worldwide and researchers identifying it is from changes in the environment, along with the type of damage created by cell phones is the same type of neurological breakdown people with MS display, the massive increase in the last 50 years in cell phone use needs to be considered as one of the potential triggering agents that has occurred in the environment creating the corresponding increase in MS.

Warning

Potential Health Effects:

Multiple Sclerosis (MS)

Chapter 8

Bipolar Disorder

Research is continuing to identify that blood-brain barrier (BBB) disruption plays a role in Alzheimer's disease and multiple sclerosis with inflammation and oxidative stress in the brain. Investigators also see that inflammation and oxidative stress are involved in the pathophysiology (source of abnormal changes) of bipolar disorder (BD).

In a 2015 study, researchers theorized that short-lived or persistent disruption of BBB integrity is associated with increased BBB permeability (leaking) and decreased central nervous system protection, so that ROS and other inflammatory substances enter the brain from the peripheral blood. This in turn leads to the activation of microglial (e.g., astrocytes) cells and promotes localized damage to oligodendrocytes and the myelin sheath, damaging myelination and nerve cell connections.[172]

Looking at psychiatric disorders, including major depressive disorder (MDD), bipolar disorder (BD) schizophrenia and autism, researchers in attempting to determine their origin are looking at the role of an increase in oxidative stress leading to neuroinflammation. These changes can stimulate microglia activation, which can contribute to brain pathology, such as that seen in MDD, BD, schizophrenia, and autism.[173] Since EMF radiation does contribute to inflammation and disruption of glia cells, it is important to investigate it as a possible contributor to these conditions.

Bipolar Disorder Incidence Increasing

Investigators utilized the National Ambulatory Medical Care Survey (1999-2003) looking at the number of patient visits in 1994-1995 compared to the number of visits during 2002-2003 that were diagnosed with bipolar disorder in 0 – 19 years old, and adults 20 years of age or older. They found increases in both age categories, especially in those under the age of 19.

Bipolar Diagnosis

	(per 100,000)	
	1994–1995	2002–2003
Youth visits (0 – 19)	25	1,003
Adults visits (20 and over)	905	1,679

From 1999 to 2003, 32% of the youth also received a diagnosis of ADHD, and 91% received some type of psychotropic medication.[174]

It is important to look at the huge increases in number of cell phone users as contributing to the increases that are being seen in these neurobiological disorders. EMF radiations from cell phones cause both leaks in the blood-brain barrier and oxidative stress. Since these conditions are being identified in bipolar disorder, cell phone use should be looked at as a possible contributor to the increase that is occurring in the diagnosis of bipolar disorder.

Warning

Potential Health Effects – abnormal changes in the brain:

Bipolar disorder diagnosis

Chapter 9

The Immune System and Cancer

EMF – Affect on the Immune System

Part of the body's immune system are different types of T cells that are called T helper 1 (Th1), T helper 2 (Th2), and T helper 17 (Th17). Both Th1 and Th2 have their own strengths to protect against bacteria, virus, and parasite pathogens. When these two systems are not in proper balance, the body is much more susceptible to all types of infections and invasions by pathogens. A 2013 study identified that EMF radiation can change the balance between these systems when they found upon EMF exposure Th1 was reduced and Th17 was increased.[175] Decreased Th1 would result in increased susceptibility to viral and bacterial infections. The role of Th17 in autoimmune disease is only beginning to be sorted out, but its being out of balance can result in diabetes, allergies, and arthritis.

Warning

Potential Health Effects – immune system imbalance:

Autoimmune diseases: unbalanced Th17
Infectious diseases: unbalanced Th1, Th2
Parasites: unbalanced Th1, Th2

After reviewing studies regarding the health effects of EMF exposure, researcher Dr. Olle Johansson of the Karolinska Institute in Sweden identified:

"EMFs disturb immune function through stimulation of various allergic and inflammatory responses, as well as effects on tissue repair processes. Such disturbances increase the risks for various diseases, including cancer. These and the EMF effects on other biological processes (e.g., DNA damage, neurological effects, etc.) are now widely reported to occur at exposure levels significantly below most current national and international safety limits."

". . . it must be concluded that the existing public safety limits are inadequate to protect public health, and that new public safety limits, as well as limits on further deployment of untested technologies, are warranted."[176]

As discussed in the section on EMF – Affect on DNA, the EMF cell phone radiation wavelength of 940 MHz creates irreversible damage to cells of the thymus gland.[177] This has implications for the body's ability to fight infections or cancers, as the thymus gland helps regulate the immune system and oversees the development of our immune system cells. It protects against viruses and bacteria. In addition, the thymus educates the cells regarding its own body's tissues and assists in preventing autoimmunity (the body attacking its own cells). Today, we have an epidemic of people with autoimmune disorders, and today's studies are showing EMF exposure could be a contributing factor.

Warning

Potential Health Effects – DNA damage:

Infections
Cancer
Autoimmune diseases
Hashimoto's disease

EMF – Affect on Cancer

There are several changes that EMF create that can give rise to the increased risk of cancer. EMF affect on toxic chemicals can lead to a greater toxicity than either chemicals or EMF would by themselves—together they become cocarcinogens, which can result in the development of cancer.[178]

EMF affect the gap junctions of the tight junction cells, and cancer cells are shown to have decreased gap junction connections. Gap junctions are designed to allow communication and selected materials to pass between cells. A decrease in these connections would create a loss of cell-to-cell communication. Communication between cells is required to regulate normal growth. As a result, the loss of cell-to-cell communication can result in cancerous changes.[179]

Researchers exposing mice to the cell phone frequency of 916 MHz for 2 hours a day for 5, 6, and 8 weeks found they develop tumors. They stated that one of the reasons other studies do not identify cancerous changes is that they are conducted for too short a time (e.g., 1 hour a day for 3 days).[180] The following are pictures of the mice from this study showing the evidence of cancerous growths.

Tumor Growth from Cell Phone Radiation

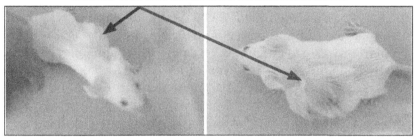

Figure 7. Mouse tumor growth.

Source: Yang L, Hao D, Wang M, et al. Cellular neoplastic transformation induced by 916 MHz microwave radiation. Figure 5. *Cell Mol Neurobiol.* 2012;32(6):1039-1046. Reprinted with kind permission from Springer Science and Business Media.

In 2015, nine German scientists published confirmation of previous findings that EMF radiation are cancer promoting. In exposing mice to no radiation as controls, and others to 0.04, 0.4 and 2 W/kg SAR, they found significantly more tumors in the liver and lungs, as well as lymphomas compared to the non-exposed mice. Since the cancers developed in the low power range of 0.04 and 0.4 SAR, which is well below exposure limits for the users of mobile phones, the investigators stated their findings established that further studies are warranted to investigate the underlying mechanisms.[181]

EMF creating imbalances in our immune system can be one of the reasons why studies show that EMF radiation has the ability to create cancer.

> **Warning**
>
> Potential Health Effects:
>
> EMF combined with chemicals = cocarcinogens
> Cell-to-cell communication lost = growth regulation lost
> Immune system imbalance
> Cancer

In a study published in the journal, *Science of the Total Environment*, Dr. Adilza Dode, et, al, identified the number of deaths from cancers in the 3rd largest city in Brazil in relation to the distance people lived from the city's 856 cell tower base stations as of 2006. Tabulating deaths for a 10 year period leading up to 2006, they identified 7,191 deaths by cancers occurred. Within an area of 500 meters (1,640 feet) from the cell towers, the mortality rate average was 34.7 per 10,000 inhabitants. The area that had the greatest concentration of cell towers (40% of the city's towers) had the greatest accumulated incidence of cancers, which was 58.3 per 10,000 in the Central-Southern region. The lowest rate was 20.5 per 10,000 in the Barreiro region, which had 5% of the city's towers.[182]

Cell Tower Distance and Number of Cancer Deaths

Closeness to Cell Towers = Greater Numbers of Cancers
Based on the Distance from Cell Towers

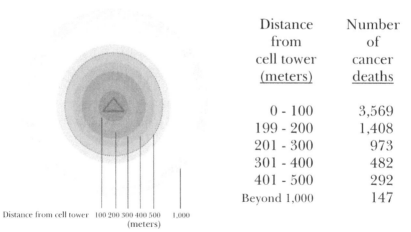

Distance from cell tower (meters)	Number of cancer deaths
0 - 100	3,569
199 - 200	1,408
201 - 300	973
301 - 400	482
401 - 500	292
Beyond 1,000	147

Distance from cell tower   100 200 300 400 500   1,000
(meters)

Figure 8. Cancer deaths based on distance from cell tower.

Cell Tower Distance and Mortality Rate

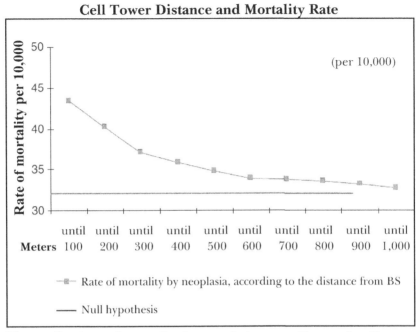

Figure 9. Rate of mortality by neoplasia, according to the distance [meters] from the base station in Belo Horizonte municipality, from 1996 to 2006, and the null hypothesis.

Source: Dode AC, Leão M, Tejo FAF, et. al. Mortality by neoplasia and cellular telephone base stations in the Belo Horizonte municipality, Minas Gerais state, Brazil. *Sci Total Environ.* 2011;409(19):3649-3665. Reprinted with permission.

As you can see from the figure and the graph, there were a greater number of cancers the closer people lived in relation to cell tower base stations. Greater than 500 meters from the towers appears to be a safer distance in regards to the risk of the development of cancers.

One of the reasons that wireless devices have been allowed to proliferate even though studies like this one clearly show the cancer dangers is that there are people who challenge results like these. Routinely, studies that identify the harm that radiation can cause are discounted, or other researchers perform a study saying they could not replicate the results. This leaves people not knowing what or who to believe. A year after this Brazil study was published, comments were published by Dr. Foster, a professor of bioengineering at University of Pennsylvania, and Lorne Trottier, an electronics engineer and Center for Inquiry science advisor, questioning their findings.[183]

In response, the authors of the Brazil study, Dr. Dode and fellow researchers, stated they believed that ". . . the authors of the critique misinterpreted our paper." Clarifying their findings with new maps that showed the correlation between the cell tower density and the number of cancers, they also stated: "We suggest that the authors of this critique refer to the May 2011 IARC (International Agency for Research on Cancer) release, which 'has classified radio-frequency electromagnetic fields as possible carcinogenic to humans (Group 2B), based on an increased risk of a glioma, a malignant type of brain cancer—237,913 new cases of brain cancers (all types combined) occurred around the world in 2008—associated with wireless phone use.'"[184]

Household Electricity

Cancers

Many studies have identified there is damage to living tissue just from the common 50 Hz and 60 Hz electrical frequencies, which have been around us since the acceptance of electricity as essential for everyday living. The damage to the DNA reveals the possibility that the increasing occurrence of cancers and many other diseases may be the result of our now total dependence on electricity for our comfortable existence, along with Wi-Fi and billions of cell phones for communication.

We are such complex beings and electricity is a variable that cannot be seen, it is very difficult to develop rigorous studies that are capable of turning out similar conclusions. However, when studies show DNA damage that does not repair, especially in immature cells, then EMF radiation can be identified as one of the precipitating causes of the cancers that are being seen in our world.

EMF create oxidation damage by generating free radicals and ROS (reactive oxygen species) that can interact with DNA resulting in single strand breaks that can become a mutation, which is one of the steps of normal cells becoming cancer cells. Researchers have been studying the affects of regular household electricity, which is 50 MHz in Europe and 60 MHz in North America, and termed ELF–EMF (extremely low frequency electromagnetic fields). After reviewing many studies that report conflicting conclusions as to the ability of ELF–EMF to produce cancers, a researcher stated: "Finally, we conclude from our review that modulations on the oxidant and antioxidant level through ELF–EMF exposure can play a causal role in cancer development."[185]

Fibroblast cells are involved in the maintenance and metabolism of connective tissue. They secret collagen, and assist wound repair. In 2002, scientists at the medical University of Vienna exposing human fibroblasts to continuous or intermittent or *pulsing* ELF–EMF 50Hz (regular house current) identified that the intermittent EMF resulted in both single and double strand breaks in DNA, with the most significant damage created by a *pulsing* of 5 minutes *on* and 10 minutes *off*. The damage was so significant the researchers concluded: "Our data strongly indicate a genotoxic [damage to DNA] potential of intermittent EMF. This points to the need of further studies in vivo [in living tissue] and consideration about environmental threshold values for ELF exposure."[186]

EMF – Affect on Brain Tumors

Brain Tumor Terminology

Since so many are being diagnosed with brain tumors today, we are including a short explanation of their terminology. A glioma is a primary brain tumor that originates from glial cells, which are supportive cells of the brain and the most common cellular component of the brain, as there are 5 to 10 times more glial cells than neurons, or nerve cells. There are three main types of glial cells; astrocytes becoming cancerous, called astrocytomas, account for 3/4 of the gliomas, followed by the less common gliomas of the other two types of glial cells, oligodendrocytes and ependymal cells.[187]

Brain Tumors from Household Electricity

Scientists after establishing that just 60 Hz causes proliferation of human astrocytoma cells stated their findings may provide a biological basis for the observed associations between magnetic fields exposure and brain tumors.[188]

Brain Tumors from Cell Phones and Cordless Phones

In 2005, scientists at the medical University of Vienna published their continuing research showing that in addition to 50 Hz, 1800 MHz of 1.2 or 2 W/kg SAR for 16 and 24 hours to either *pulsing* 5 minutes *on* and 10 minutes *off*, or to continuous wave, induced DNA single- and double-strand breaks in both human fibroblasts and rat female reproductive cells. They reported that the intermittent, pulsing exposure showed a stronger effect than continuous exposure. In addition, they concluded that the DNA damage was not due to the affects from the heat generated.[189]

This study's findings are important as there has been an embedded belief over the years that the only damage from EMF radiation is from the ability of the radiation to increase temperature in tissues, and as long as there is no increase in temperature there is no damage.

As a result, there have been accusations that the data in the above University of Vienna study was fraudulent, accompanied with requests that the paper be withdrawn from the publication.[190] In 2010, the editors of *Mutagenic Research* stated, after submission by one of the lead authors of the original study that the doubts raised about their findings did not apply, the journal decided it would not withdraw the research from their publication, and leave the discussion open to scientific debate.[191]

In 2009, researchers performed a meta-analysis of the studies that had been published regarding brain tumors. They identified that greater than 10 years of cell phone use results in a doubled risk of brain tumors (gliomas) on same side of head as the person holds the phone.[192]

In studies published in September and December 2012, Drs. Hardell, Hansson Mild, and Carlberg performed an analysis on studies of over 1,000 brain cancer cases looking at the association of brain tumors with cell phone and cordless phone use. Their calculations revealed that use of a mobile phone resulted in a significantly greater incidence for brain tumors on the side of the head the person holds the phone against. They also reported an increased incidence for cordless phone use. Taking about 10 years for the tumors to develop, they found there is a greater risk with more cumulative hours used, with highest risk in those who had used the phones for more than 400 hours. Of great concern for children, they found one of the highest risks is for those whose first use of a wireless phone was before the age of 20.[193] Based on their findings these researchers expressing concern concluded:

> "Some studies show increasing incidence of brain tumors whereas other studies do not. It is concluded that one should be careful using incidence data to dismiss results in analytical epidemiology. The IARC* carcinogenic classification does not seem to have had any significant impact on governments' perceptions of their responsibilities to protect public health from this widespread source of radiation."[194]

*International Agency for Research on Cancer at World Health Organization.

This statement is important to keep in mind, as it is clear the governments of the world are not taking the necessary steps to implement procedures and guidelines that will protect our health. This means that we each have to become our own health care advocates by educating ourselves and taking the actions that are necessary to protect ourselves and our families from the many unknown radiations surrounding us 24 hours a day, which we were never provided the opportunity to decline.

In 2014, published in the *International Journal of Environmental Research and Public Health*, Carlberg and Hardell made a greater plea to review the present guidelines of what is considered safe EMF exposure based on their continued analysis of patients with glioma tumors and identifying they have statistically decreased survival. The researchers are advocating that: ". . . RF–EMF should be regarded as human carcinogen requiring urgent revision of current exposure guidelines."[195]

In 2015, continuing to identify the cancer risk, Hardell and Carlberg published further confirmation of the results of the connection of cell phone and cordless phone use to brain tumors. Looking at two case-control studies on patients between 20 – 80 years old diagnosed with brain cancer between 1997 and 2009, they found that both cell phone and cordless phone use significantly increases the risk of glioma cell tumors on the side of the brain the cell phone is held against. They found most tumors were in the temporal lobe of the brain, which is on the side of head next to the ear where the phones are held. Important for children, they continued to identify a higher risk of tumors for users before the age of 20 compared to older age groups.[196]

Warning

Potential Health Effects:

Brain Cancer

EMF – Affect on Breast Cancer

Young women who carry cell phones in their bras are developing breast cancer. Doctors from the University of California, Irvine published a study detailing near identical breast cancer tumors from 4 women who stated they had carried their cell phones in their bras while jogging or using their blue tooth. One of the reasons they published these case studies is that none of the women had a family history of breast cancer, and all were negative for the BRCA 1 / BRCA 2 genes, which have been thought to indicate a greater risk for developing breast cancer. Without these increased risk factors, it is rare for women under 40 to develop breast cancer. Two of the women were 21 years old, one reported keeping her cell phone in her bra for several hours a day, and the other stated she kept her cell phone in her bra for 8 hours a day for 6 years. A 33 year old kept her cell phone in her bra while jogging 3 – 4 times a week for 8 years, while a 39 year old talked for hours a day on Bluetooth with her cell phone in her bra while commuting for 10 years.

The researchers highlight the importance of understanding that the safety limits for the power of cell phones and their potential harm have not been adequately studied. The FCC allows 1.6 watts per kilogram (W/kg) of tissue SAR (specific absorption rate) as the maximum limit, and any cell phone that tests below 1.6 is considered safe. However, the researchers argue that:

"The duration of exposure during a SAR test is only 30 minutes and does not reflect the total amount of EMR exposure consumers experience with more prolonged exposure. Furthermore, FCC guidelines do not address the issue of risks associated with direct skin contact with cellular phones. This is a critical issue, as the long-term consequence of the direct thermal effect of EMR on developing breast tissue for extended duration has not been documented. In addition, unlike older cellular devices, smartphones have the ability to regularly transmit information, sending and receiving an intermittent signal even when the user of the device is not actively handling it. The accumulation of this passive exposure to EMR is also not well studied."[197]

Several researchers have theorized that both EMF radiation and light at night, each decreasing melatonin, might contribute to the formation of breast cancers.[198] Dr. Mytill Simkó, a cellular and molecular biology researcher at the Austrian Institute of Technology concluded:

"The so-called melatonin hypothesis describe that EMF suppress the level of melatonin synthesis; this reduced level of melatonin could function as a possible amplifier leading to an increased cancer risk. Based on several lines of investigations, it is suggested that EMF exposure is able to perform cell type–dependent activation by means of increasing levels of free radicals. Those EMF-induced reactions could lead to a higher incidence of DNA damage and, therefore, to an increased risk of tumor development."[199]

The WHO's (World Health Organization) International Agency for Research on Cancer (IARC) published the latest world cancer statistics stating: "Global cancer burden rises to 14.1 million new cases in 2012: Marked increase in breast cancers must be addressed." Utilizing the headline: "Sharp Rise in Breast Cancer Worldwide," their statistics show that since the 2008 estimates, breast cancer incidence has increased by more than 20%. There is more breast cancer in the developed countries, with the highest incidence rates in western Europe at more than 90 new cases per 100,000 women annually, compared with 30 per 100,000 found in eastern Africa.[200] More breast cancers in developed countries identifies that it is increasing as a result of the environment. Based on how EMF damage DNA, it is important to recognize wireless radiation as a major contributing factor.

Chapter 10

Major Organ Damage – Heart, Kidney, Bladder, Skin

EMF – Heart Tissue Damage

Myocardium EMF Radiation Damage

In 2005, researchers exposing rats to 900 MHz mobile phone radiation identified the radiation induces oxidative heart tissue damage. They found the biochemical oxidation markers MDA and NO increased, and SOD, CAT, and GSH-Px* decreased, changes that identify oxidation has occurred.[201]

*(MDA) malondialdehyde, (NO) nitric oxide, (SOD) superoxide dismutase, (CAT) catalase, and (GSH-Px) glutathione peroxidase.]

Scientists continue to reveal that our standard household electricity has been affecting us over the years. Since it is cumulative, the increase we are seeing on every front from cell phones and Wi-Fi devices, along with their need to increase the proliferation of cell phone and communication towers and antennas, has added a burden on the body that is showing up in greater numbers of people.

Published in 2013, tests on rats that were exposed to standard 50 Hz EMF, for 4 hours a day 7 days a week for 2 months, revealed that the myocardium (the middle muscular layer of the heart wall) showed evidence of damage created by oxidative stress. The change included degeneration of the mitochondria, which produce the cells' energy and therefore the heart has reduced energy capacity to perform its important job of providing oxygen throughout the entire body.[202]

EMF – Kidney Tissue Damage

Researchers exposed rats to 900 MHz, 1800 MHz, and 2.45 GHz Wi-Fi and mobile phone frequencies for 60 minutes a day during pregnancy and the offspring to 6 weeks of age. After examining kidney tissue taken from the rats during the 4th, 5th, and 6th weeks of the experiment, the researchers stated they identified that EMR caused oxidative damage that results in injury to the kidneys in growing rats.[203]

Researchers exposing rats to cell phone radiation of 900 MHz looked at the urinary markers (MDA and NAG) [MDA malondialdehyde; NAG N-actyl-B-D-glucosaminidase] that show that oxidation has occurred, and found that the change in the markers was consistent of oxidation damage to the kidney tubules of the rats. They gave one group of rats caffeic acid phenethyl ester (CAPE), a flavonoid (antioxidant) like compound, which is one of the major components of honeybee propolis that acts like a potent free radical scavenger and antioxidant. It was found to be protective against the EMF oxidative kidney damage.[204]

These same researchers also looked at CAPE compared to melatonin, and found that melatonin was more protective of the kidney tissue when compared to CAPE.[205] As discussed in the section on EMF – Affect on Sleep / Insomnia, melatonin functions as an antioxidant. In this role, it protects the cells from DNA damage and reduces the risk of the development of tumors.

Another group of researchers also found that 900 MHz radiation caused oxidation damage in kidneys. They provided one of their groups with vitamin C that was successful in preventing the damage, damage that persisted in the EMF exposed group that did not receive the vitamin C.[206]

EMF – Bladder Irritation

One of the conditions that is being increasingly seen in people who are seeking help with their electromagnetic sensitivity problems is an irritable, burning bladder, with some stating that they have been diagnosed with interstitial cystitis. A study published in 2014 sheds light on one of the reasons people are suffering from these conditions. Subjecting rats to 8 hours a day of EMF radiation for 20 days and then microscopically looking at their bladder cells, they found evidence of severe inflammation compared to rats that were not subjected to the radiation. Their findings prompted them to conclude: "Intensive use of mobile phones has negative impact on bladder tissue as well as the other organs." They recommend that reducing use of mobile phones for those with any inflammatory condition will help bring the symptoms under control.[207]

EMF – Skin and Tissue Damage

Stated earlier, EMF disrupt calcium balance in the cells. Research shows that calcium is necessary for the normal development of skin cells as they mature and migrate to the skin's surface to eventually be shed. Without the normal calcium gradient, the cells do not advance through their normal differentiation cycle and they cannot perform their critical barrier function of protection, nor can they recover their barrier function once disrupted.[208] Since EMF disrupt calcium balance within and outside the cells, this study identifying that the skin can no longer act like a barrier helps reveal why so many people developed rashes and hive like reactions in their skin when utility smart meters were installed in their neighborhoods, or when they utilize cell phones or computers, or watch television.

Skin Rashes

The researchers in the study in the section on EMF – Affect on Itching / Tingling / Burning Skin / Rashes revealing that mast cells in the skin degranulate causing itching and bleeding upon

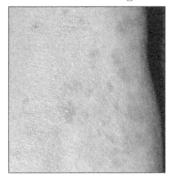

exposure to EMF combined with pesticides stated:

"Considering the biological importance of mast cells in cutaneous [skin] immune reactions, future studies should reveal whether combined exposures to chemical and physical environmental agents pose a serious health risk."[209]

This study also identifies the importance of additional chemical interactions because we all have a plethora of toxic chemicals in our bodies that can interact with EMF radiation, creating more harm than the chemicals or the EMF would by themselves.

Signs of skin reactions to electromagnetic radiation have been with us right in the midst of the unprecedented roll out of electromagnetic technologies. In 1994 Dr. Olle Johannson and fellow researchers investigated the itchy skin rashes, termed *screen dermatitis*, that were being identified in some people upon exposure to video display terminals (VDTs). Looking at mark-ers in the skin that would help identify why some people were experiencing *screen dermatitis*, Dr. Olle Johansson and colleagues from the Department of Neuroscience, Karolinska Institute in Sweden used the exposure of an ordinary TV set with 2 patients who experienced skin itch, heat sensation, pain, erythema (red-dening), papules (inflamed elevation) and pustules (inflamed el-evation with pus) due to working at VDTs. They found a very high number of histamine-positive mast cells, as well as a high number of somatostatin-immunoreactive dendritic cells, in neck skin biopsies taken before the start of the exposure. After the TV exposure, the number of mast cells was the same; but the soma-tostatin-positive cells disappeared. They theorized that the high number of mast cells present may explain the clinical symptoms of itching, pain, edema and erythema. Their conclusion was that these symptoms people are experiencing have to be taken seri-ously.[210]

In 1996, Dr. Johansson and fellow colleagues looked at skin from *screen dermatitis* sufferers to find a common biochemical marker that could be used to determine why they had symptoms and others do not. Even though the samples they were examining were not marked, *screen dermatitis* or non-reactive people, they found the *screen dermatitis* skin to be so differing, they could blindly separate the two groups from each other. They also identified a group of markers in the sufferers that were similar.[211]

In 1997, Drs. Gangi and Johansson continued further research due to the increasing numbers saying that they develop problems with their skin, as well as symptoms from certain internal organs, such as the central nervous system (CNS) and the heart, when they are close to electric equipment. Most of these patients use VDTs and claim to have skin symptoms, such as pain, itch, heat sensation, erythema, papules, and pustules. The CNS symptoms they report of dizziness, tiredness, and headache are what people state they experience after smart meters are put on their homes. Identifying that the redness, itch, heat sensation, edema, and pain are also common symptoms of sunburn (UV dermatitis), they found changes in cell populations of the skin of patients suffering from *screen dermatitis* are similar to other sufferers, and are similar to those created by damage due to ultraviolet (UV) light as well as ionizing (x-ray or nuclear) radiation, except they found that *screen dermatitis* patients have a much higher number of mast cells. They reasoned that since they know UVB irradiation induces mast cell degranulation, the high number of mast cells present in the *screen dermatitis* patients and the possible release of specific substances, such as histamine, may explain their clinical symptoms of itch, pain, edema and erythema. There are changes of other cells after exposure to UVB and ionizing radiation (e.g., Langerhans' cells disappear, which also occur in *screen dermatitis* patients. These changes led the researchers to conclude there is a common cellular and molecular basis for the changes that occur with all 3 types of radiation.[212]

In 2000, Drs. Gangi and Johansson published a study confirming that EMF affect mast cells causing them to degranulate, which along with other substances release histamine that triggers an allergic hypersensitivity response of, itch, edema, and local redness. The EMF also affect dendritic cells, which release somatostatin that can create the subjective sensations of on-going inflammation and sensitivity to ordinary lights that some with *screen dermatitis* also experience.[213]

In 2001 after Dr. Olle Johannson identified the histamine mast cell degranulation in *screen dermatitis* sufferers, he teamed with other researchers and found that histamine-containing mast cells of almost 40% of normal healthy volunteers also moved up in the layers of skin and degranulated in the skin exposed to visual display terminals and ordinary television sets.[214]

The EMF trigger the cells in the skin into a cascade of reactions. The researchers so far have not yet identified if they all happen at once, or whether mast cell activation then triggers the other cells to react. Whatever the exact sequence, those who suffer with itching skin around electronics and wireless devices deserve to know that there are biochemically identifiable changes the EMF create in the skin that cause their allergic type reactions.

Histamine Skin Injury

A 2012 study identifies why skin eruptions can occur upon exposure to EMF, with the subsequent opening of the mast cells in the skin and the release of the histamine from the granules they contain. They found that histamine in the skin results in loss of the layer of cells in the skin that are responsible for the skin's barrier protection. It also results in the thinning of the epidermis (outer layer of skin). The researchers stated: "Our findings suggest a new mechanism by which mast cell activation and histamine release contribute to skin barrier defects in inflammatory skin diseases."[215]

Other skin changes have been investigated by researchers citing radiation is primarily absorbed by the skin. They exposed two groups of rats to 900 MHz cell phone radiation 30 minutes a day for 10 days, providing one group with melatonin and one without. Compared with the control group that was not exposed, the skin of the radiated group without melatonin showed:

1.   Layers of increased thickness
2.   Atrophy (deterioration) of the epidermis (outer skin layer)
3.   Increased numbers of basal cells (basal cell carcinoma is a frequently occurring skin cancer)
4.   Capillary proliferation
5.   Impairment in collagen tissue distribution (decreased collagen results in skin drooping and looking aged)
6.   Separation of collagen bundles in the dermis (sensitive layer of skin below the epidermis)

None of these changes occurred in the group provided with the melatonin.[216] With reduced melatonin occurring due to cell phone exposure, our bodies cannot assist with repairing these negative changes in the skin when we are exposed to cell phones. The combination of reducing exposure to the EMF radiation so that there is less of a reduction in melatonin, and possibly taking melatonin could assist healing the skin reactions people are experiencing upon exposure to EMF radiation. (For more information on melatonin, see section on EMF – Affect on Sleep / Insomnia.)

> **Warning**
> Potential Health Effects – on skin:
> Hives, rashes, itching, and bleeding

Vitamin D and C

Vitamin D is also needed for the calcium gradient to function in its role of assisting the differentiation of keratinocytes, which helps the skin to perform its role as a protective barrier.[217] The pandemic of vitamin D deficiency that has occurred since sunlight has been deemed harmful and use of sunscreens massively promoted, would add to the likelihood of people who are unable to develop the protective barrier their skin is designed to provide.

Working with a rat epidermal (outer layer of skin) cell line, researchers have also identified that like vitamin D, vitamin C also assists in the gradient maturation of a normal protective skin barrier.[218] These studies show taking vitamin D and C supplements would assist in reducing skin reactions caused by EMF radiations.

EMF – Damage Living Tissue

Scientists exposing plants to 900 MHz found their responses similar to a wound response, which led them to the conclusion that the plants perceive the radiation as an injurious stimulus. Based on this, the researchers stated:

> "Taken as a whole, the data provide new evidence supporting the hypothesis that plants perceive and respond to microwave irradiation as though it was an injurious treatment. Even though the RF-EMF is non-thermal and the total power we used very low (0.1 W dissipated in 200 m^3), the similarities with wounding (leaf-pricking, burning and cutting) are striking."[219]

These results show that living tissues respond to EMF the same as they would to being cut, burned, or pricked. In other words, EMF radiation injures living tissue.

A group of researchers creating an amputation model in rats exposed them to a RF-EMF antenna that delivered an average power density that equaled 128 feet (39 m) from a 915 MHz cell phone tower (SAR = 756 mW/m2) for 10 minutes, one time per week for 8 weeks. They found that RF-EMF radiation serves as a trigger for pain in areas where nerves have been cut. They also stated their results suggested that those who have suffered from a nerve injury or other types of peripheral nerve pathology may be prone to RF-EMF induced pain. Their experiment identified that the animals not subjected to surgery showed no response to RF-EMF. They also saw dramatic and sustained shifts in the calcium concentration within the cells. Additionally, they found the new nerve fibers that developed in repairing the wounds are either unmyelinated or only thinly myelinated. This highlights the importance of the protective myelin sheath. Further research on oxidative stress resulting in the loss of the protective myelin sheath on nerve cells could help elucidate the great variability of responses to EMF radiation. They concluded: "Thus, this study offers a possible explanation for contradicting accounts on evoked pain by RF-EMF and highlights nerve pathology [damage] as the crucial contributing factor to RF-EMF-induced symptoms." They also stated their findings may prove valuable in developing a patient's pain management protocol, particularly for those who have lost a limb.[220]

This identification of EMF having the ability to cause cellular changes and pain where there has been tissue and nerve damage, brings further clarification regarding variable responses to EMF radiation exposure. One of the important variable factors of whether people feel symptoms in an EMF field could be whether they have had a physical injury, surgical procedures, or as this article identifies, loss of a limb.

Warning

Potential Health Effects – on injuries or surgeries:

Increased pain

Radiations enter injured area

Chapter 11

Diabetes, Obesity, and Anorexia

EMF – Affect on Diabetes

The rats in the study discussed in EMF – Affect on Short-term Memory / Alzheimer's that were exposed to a 900 MHz cell phone frequency 30 minutes a day in talking mode, during their whole prenatal period and first 80 days of life, revealed that EMF radiation affects blood sugar. The exposed rats developed a pre-diabetic blood glucose of 132 mg/dl (milligrams per deciliter) compared to the control group of rats that were not exposed to the cell phone radiation and maintained a normal blood glucose level of 96 mg/dl.[221] In addition to identifying harmful changes to the brain, this study confirms that EMF radiation increases blood sugar. These results are shown in the following chart.

Cell Phone Radiation Increases Blood Glucose (Sugar)

Rats	Blood Glucose
Sham (no cell phone exposure)	96 mg/dl*
Exposed to 900 MHz	132 mg/dl*

* mg/dl = milligrams per deciliter

Source: Celikozlu SD, Ozyurt MS, Cimbiz A, Yardimoglu MY, Cayci MK, Ozay Y. The effects of long term exposure of magnetic field via 900-MHz GSM radiation on some biochemical parameters and brain histology in rats. *Electromagn Biol Med.* 2012;31(4):344-355.

EMF effects are of particular importance for diabetics as they are more vulnerable to the EMF affecting their blood-brain barrier (BBB). In 1995, researchers identified that the blood-brain barrier in diabetic rats is more vulnerable to permeability (leakage).[222] This was confirmed in a study published in 2004, when normal and diabetic rats were subjected to a 50 Hz magnetic field for 8 hours a day for 21 days. Researchers identified that diabetic rats showed an increase in their blood-brain barrier permeability resulting from the magnetic field exposure, which did not occur in the rats with normal blood sugar metabolism.[223]

Dr. Magda Havas has identified that EMF affect blood sugar in type 1 diabetics (insufficient insulin production). When they are in an electrically clean environment, they need less insulin. Type 2 diabetics (ineffective use of insulin) also show the connection as they experience a rise in their blood sugar when exposed to indoor wiring. This EMF blood sugar connection creates the possibility that diabetics may not gain as much benefit by exercising on EMF emitting devices, such as treadmills. In measuring the blood sugar of a woman with type 2 diabetes after walking for 20 to 30 minutes on a treadmill her blood sugar went up, compared with her blood sugar going down after walking for the same amount of time in a mall.[224]

Warning

Potential Health Effects – on blood sugar:

Increased blood sugar
Increased incidence of diabetes
Increased difficulty controlling blood sugar

EMF and Sunscreens – Affect on Obesity

The body mass index (BMI) is currently utilized to make a determination whether a person is obese, and is calculated by dividing the person's weight by their height. A BMI between 20 – 25 is considered a normal weight for maintaining good health. A BMI between 25 – 30 is classified as overweight, and greater than 30 is the definition of obese, with Obese Class I defined as 30 – 35, Class II 35 – 40, and Class III is a BMI greater than 40. These ranges can vary depending on the country.[225]

We have seen a dramatic shift in the numbers of people today who are classified as obese. In the United States, the percentage of the population classified as obese has grown dramatically since the 1970s, when cell phones and sunscreens were introduced. The changes in the American population can be seen in the following table.

American Obesity Rates in Percentages

Age groups	1970s	2010
6 – 11 year olds	4.0%	18.8%
12 – 19 year olds	6.0%	18.1%
Adults (20 and over)	13 – 17%	36.0%

Source: American Heart Association website. Statistical Fact Sheet 2013 Update. Retrieved March 11, 2013 from: www.heart. org/idc/groups/heart-public/@wcm/@sop/@smd/documents/downloadable/ucm_319588.pdf

Both the use of sunscreens and EMF radiating devices are capable of contributing to the growing obesity epidemic. Sunscreen chemicals are similar in structure to a class of chemicals labeled as *obesegens* (foreign chemicals that alter how the body metabolizes fat and lead to obesity). They alter a person's fat metabolism pathways so that the person can be careful of their diet, but struggle throughout their lives attempting to maintain a normal weight. The prolific use of sunscreens can be contributing to the obesity epidemic. For more detail, please see *Sunscreens – Biohazard: Treat As Hazardous Waste* published in 2012 and available at: www.SunscreensBiohazard.com.

An additional compounding problem of blocking the sun's beneficial rays with sunscreen has been identified in a study published in the medical journal *Diabetes* in 2014. Researching whether vitamin D alone, or UV-B ultraviolet radiation (the sunlight radiation that sunscreens block) would show signs of reducing weight gain and diabetic risk factors, their results established that vitamin D supplementation had no effect. They found working with mice fed a high-fat diet, that it is UV-B ultraviolet radiation that significantly reduced the risk factors of weight gain, glucose intolerance, insulin resistance, nonalcoholic fatty liver disease measures, and blood levels of fasting insulin, glucose, and cholesterol. In determining why the ultraviolet radiation was more beneficial than vitamin D alone, they found that the role of the nitric oxide (NO) created by the UV-B radiation in the skin may be the important factor of sunlight's role in reducing the risk of obesity and diabetic risk factors.[226]

This would indicate that direct sunlight is more beneficial than vitamin D supplementation in reducing obesity.

Based on evidence such as this, in attempting to reverse the steadily increasing percentage of people who are now classified as obese and diabetic, it is important to reconsider the campaign to use sunscreen that began with their introduction in the 1970s, which has been promoted as having the ability to reduce the risks of skin cancers and melanoma.

However, this is not the case. In April, 2014, BBC News posted an article entitled: "Skin cancer rates 'surge since 1970s.'" In England, the incidence has grown five times since sunscreens were introduced, climbing to 13,000 diagnosed with melanoma today, up from only 1,800 diagnosed in the 1970s.[227]

The following graph shows the dramatic increase in melanoma in the United States and the years UVB, UVA, and nano/microparticle titanium dioxide and zinc oxide sunscreens were introduced.

Melanoma – U.S. Incidence Rates

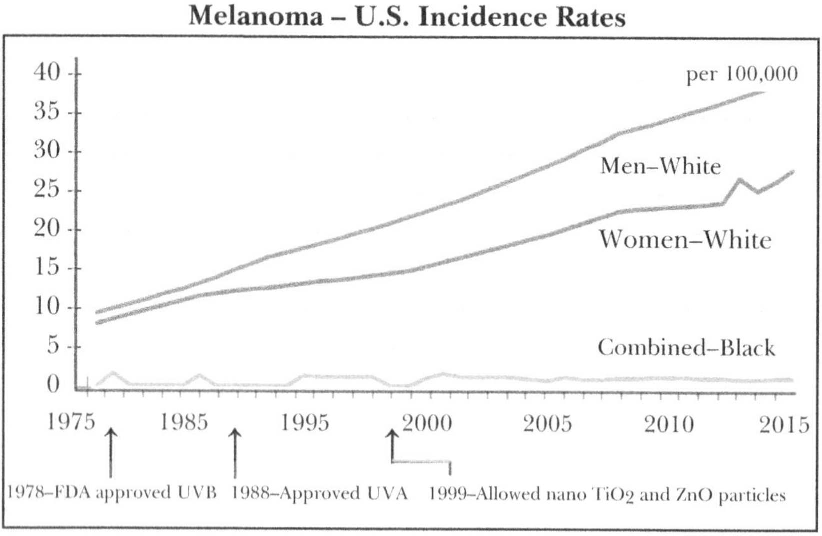

Figure 10. Melanoma incidence rates between 1975 and 2015.

Sources: NIH National Cancer Institute website. Cancer Statistics: Fast Facts. Retrieved September 18, 2018 from: www.seer. cancer.gov/faststats/selections.php?

Between 1975 and 2015, melanoma incidence among whites males in the United States rose from 9.5 in 1975 to 40.1 per 100,000 in 2015. For white women, their incidence rate rose from 8.1 in 1975 to 28.1 per 100,000 in 2015.[228] If sunscreen use reduced the risk of melanoma development, these statistics should have been going down over the last 40 years since they were introduced, rather than the increase in melanoma that is being identified. The incidence rate has not changed much for those who have more melanin in their skin, such as Asians and Blacks, as melanin is one of the best solar protections for our skin. This is why for whites the protective response of the body to solar radiation exposure results in tanning (increased melanin) of the skin.

What was also introduced in the 1970s were cell phones. Drs. Hallberg and Johansson, after identifying that increases in head and neck melanomas occurred after FM/television broadcasting networks were installed in European countries, put forth the theory that the radio radiation may exacerbate the cancerous changes in the cells caused by solar radiation.[229] With cell phones held to the head, it could also be why there has been an increase in head and neck melanomas.

We again have the makings of a perfect storm—chemical sunscreens combining with radiations from FM antennas as well as cell phones, making them cocarcinogens (cancer producing). Also, sunscreens only block UV and let people stay in the sun longer than is safe, as they do not develop the warning sign of a sunburn. However, they cannot block the greater amount of near infrared radiation that penetrates much deeper and results in more damage to the cells than UV.

It is time we heed the advice of Drs. C.F. and F.C. Garland of UCSD and Dr. E.D. Gorham of the Naval Health Research Center, San Diego who in 1993 in the *Annals of Epidemiology* stated: "Traditional means of limiting overexposure to the sun, such as wearing of hats and adequate clothing and avoidance of prolonged sunbathing, may be more prudent than reliance on chemical sunscreens."[230]

EMF – Affect on Anorexia

Studies on laboratory animals have identified that loss of GABA is implicated in a reduction of food intake to the point of starvation. They have determined there is a GABA signaling network that governs appetite and food palatability. As a result, proper functioning of GABA is important for food intake and necessary to maintain normal feeding behavior to prevent anorexia.[231]

In a study published in 2013, Dr. Nicole Barbarich-Marsteller in association with other researchers stated it is critical to understand the biochemistry behind anorexia as: ". . . anorexia nervosa has one of the highest mortality rates among psychiatric disorders with limited effective treatments." On investigating rats, they found that anorexia type behavior is associated with a "profound reduction" in cells developing in the hippocampus region of the brain.[232] Since EMF reduce the number of cells in the hippocampus, as well as reduce GABA functioning, then anorexia behavior is another possible outcome of excess exposure to EMF radiation.

Warning

Potential Health Effect – decreased hippocampus cells decreased GABA:

Anorexia

Part 3

Impact on the Next Generations

Chapter 12

The Impact on the Reproductive Tract:
Sex Organs / Fertility / Pregnancy / Development

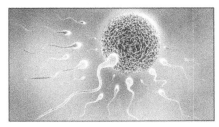

Both the male and the female reproductive tracts are susceptible to damage by EMF radiation. All the scientific evidence that
is detailed in this section of the book reveals without a doubt that
our massive adoption of wire-
less devices, before research
was completed to assure that
they are safe for living tissues,
is jeopardizing the future of
not only our children, but
also the generations to come.

EMF – Affect on Male and Female Reproductive Organs

In looking at studies
of reproductive organs,
researchers in 2013 came
to the conclusion that:

> ". . . the results of cur-
> rent studies indicate
> that oxidative stress
> from exposure to Wi-Fi

and mobile phone-induced EMR is a significant mechanism
affecting female and male reproductive systems."[233]

The following diagram identifies that EMF radiation impacts
every aspect of reproduction, from fertilization through pregnancy, and the critical development of the fetus.

Effects of Electromagnetic Fields (EMF) on Reproduction

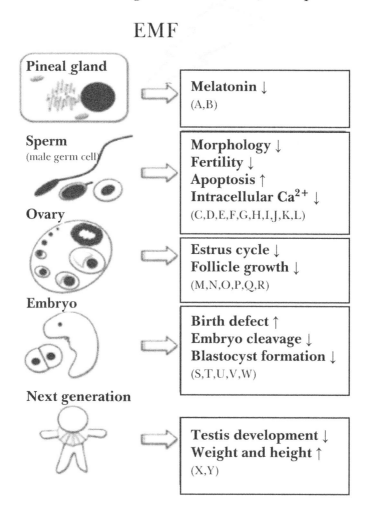

EMF

Pineal gland

Melatonin ↓
(A,B)

Sperm
(male germ cell)

Ovary

Morphology ↓
Fertility ↓
Apoptosis ↑
Intracellular Ca^{2+} ↓
(C,D,E,F,G,H,I,J,K,L)

Estrus cycle ↓
Follicle growth ↓
(M,N,O,P,Q,R)

Embryo

Birth defect ↑
Embryo cleavage ↓
Blastocyst formation ↓
(S,T,U,V,W)

Next generation

Testis development ↓
Weight and height ↑
(X,Y)

Legend: ↑ increase ↓ decrease or inhibition

Figure 11: Summary of the effects of electromagnetic fields (EMF) on reproduction.

Source: Gye MC, Park CJ. Effect of electromagnetic field exposure on the reproductive system. *Clin Exp Reprod Med*. 2012;39(1):1-9. (Also see footnote[234] for contributions used to generate diagram.) Reprinted with permission.

Designing studies is difficult as this article summarized that EMF effects differ due to the frequency, duration, and strength, leading the researchers to conclude:

"Thus, it would be better to avoid or minimize casual exposure to EMFs during pregnancy."

"The effort to avoid EMF exposure and techniques to protect or relieve EMF radiation are required to preserve our reproductive potential."[235]

EMF – Sex Hormone Reduction

Men: Decreased Testosterone

Cell phone radiations lower men's testosterone. Exposing rats to the cell phone frequency of 900 MHz for 2 hours a day for 45 days leads to a reduction in their testosterone levels. Exposed rats had testosterone levels of 176 ng/dl compared to the non-exposed rats levels averaging 505 ng/dl.

Rats	Testosterone levels
Sham (no cell phone exposure)	505 ng/dl*
Exposed to 900 MHz	176 ng/dl*

*ng/dl = nanograms per deciliter

Source: Kesari KK, Behari J. Evidence for mobile phone radiation exposure effects on reproductive pattern of male rats: role of ROS. *Electomagn Biol Med*. 2013;31(3):213-222.

Women: Decreased Progesterone

Studying 180 female workers exposed to EMF for 1 year compared to 349 controls, researchers found the radiation led to a significant increase in menstrual disorders, increased menorrhagia (heavy bleeding), and a reduction in progesterone levels. Progesterone is needed to balance the estrogenic build up of the uterine lining. When progesterone is decreased the result can be increased heavy bleeding.

Menstrual Disorders – Menorrhagia

	Menstrual disorders	Menorrhagia (heavy bleeding)	Reduced progesterone
Controls	12%	8%	3.8 mg/L
EMF exposed	27 – 34%	16.9%	2.1 – 2.4 mg/L*

*mg/L = milligrams per liter

Source: Xu YQ, Li BH, Cheng HM. High-frequency electromagnetic field exposure on reproductive and endocrine functions of female workers. *Zhonghua Lao Dong Wei Sheng Zhi Ye Bing Za Zhi.* 2008;26(6):332-335.

EMF – Affect on Female Reproductive Organs

Measuring oxidation markers in the endometrium (inner wall of the uterus) of rats exposed to 900 MHz for 30 minutes a day for 30 days showed the uterus did undergo oxidation damage, as well as it created an infusion with white blood cells (the body's protective response). The researchers concluded that the 900 MHz mobile phone radiation induced endometrial impairment, creating damage at both the biochemical and histological (cellular) levels.[236]

EMF – Affect on Male Reproductive Tract

Researchers exposed pregnant rats and their offspring to 900 MHz, 1800 MHz (1.8 GHz), and 2.45 GHz Wi-Fi and mobile phone frequencies 60 minutes a day during pregnancy and their first 6 weeks of growth. They examined male testis tissue taken from the male offspring rats during the 4th, 5th, and 6th weeks of the experiment. The researchers identified that EMR caused oxidative damage to the testicles in growing rats, which they stated may induce precocious puberty (puberty occurring at an unusually early age).[237]

Testicular Cell Death

Researchers who exposed 12 week-old rats to 2.45 MHz for 60 minutes a day for 28 days identified statistically significant differences in spermatogenesis (creation of sperm for fertilization) and apoptosis (death of testicular tissue) compared to groups not exposed to the radiation.[238]

Abnormal Sperm

Rats exposed to cell phone radiation of 900 MHz and 1.8 GHz for 1 hour a day for 28 days exhibited increased reactive oxygen species (ROS) throughout the male reproductive tract, which are indicators of oxidation damage. The testis and epididymis (testis ducts that hold sperm during maturation) had a decrease in glutathione (GSH) and an increase in malondialdehyde (MDA), indicating they were being subjected to increased oxidation. These researchers also identified that EMF radiation decreases sperm motility, which decreases the possibility of fertilization.[239]

	Sperm Motility
In controls	72%
In exposed animals	43%

Source: Mailankot M, Kunnath AP, Javalekshmi H, Koduru B, Valsalan R. Radio frequency electromagnetic radiation (RF–EMR) from GSM (0.9/1.8GHz) mobile phones induces oxidative stress and reduces sperm motility in rats. *Clinics* (Sao Paulo). 2009;64(6):561-565.

A 2013 review of studies looking at possible male reproductive organ harm identified that mobile phone or microwave radiations are very harmful. There are increased levels of reactive oxygen species (ROS) that produce oxidation damage in the testis, which can result in mutagenic changes in reproductive patterns and lead to infertility. They also cause biological damage, decreased sperm count, enzymatic and hormonal changes, DNA damage, and apoptosis (cell self-destruction or cell death). All these changes can result in testicular infertility or testicular cancer.[240]

The section on EMF – Affect on the Blood-brain Barrier described tight junction cells. There are similar connecting cells that act as a pathway modifying the cell's membrane to allow passage of selected chemicals to pass between cells. These specific connectors are called connexins. They are specialized proteins that perform as gap junctions, and as such are essential for transportation of chemicals and cell-to-cell communication. Just as the tight junction cells are susceptible to EMF disruption, so are connexins.[241]

Connexins are distributed throughout the testes and in different structures of the male genital tract (epididymis, seminal vesicle, prostate, corpus cavernosum–erectile tissues of the penis). They play crucial roles in the control of sperm development.[242] Disruption in these important structures could be one of the reasons for the decreased and malfunctioning sperm identified in the following studies.

In 2012, a review examined the results of the studies that have been conducted in rats, mice, and rabbits exposed to cell phone frequency radiations for variable lengths of time. The researchers stated the results of these studies show that EMF decrease sperm count and motility, and increase oxidative stress. Studies on human spermatozoa directly exposed to EMF show they have decreased motility, abnormalities in size and shape, as well as increased oxidative stress. In evaluating the sperm of men who utilized cell phones, they showed decreased numbers of sperm, and decreased motility (particularly rapid progressive ability to travel). They did have normal shape, but had decreased survival. Importantly, the researchers determined that the abnormalities in the sperm were directly related to the duration of mobile phone use.[243]

These results were further proven in a 2012 study that exposed rats to 1 GHz (1000 MHz) for 2 hours day for 45 days. The rats showed several altered reproductive parameters, as well as reduced melatonin resulting from EMF radiation. The researchers concluded:

"These results are indications of deleterious effects of these radiations on the reproductive pattern of male rats."[244]

Several of these researchers exposed rats to mobile phone frequency radiation for 2 hours a day for 35 days. They identified significant changes to the sperm cell cycle and the formation of abnormal nuclei (cell nucleus), creating what they determined were clear indications of an infertility pattern, which arose from the generation of reactive oxygen species (the harmful ROS discussed in the section EMF – Affect on Antioxidant Balance). They stated:

"It is concluded that radiofrequency electromagnetic wave from commercially available cell phones might affect the fertilizing potential of spermatozoa."[245]

Upon exposing 70 day-old rats to 10 GHz (10,000 MHz) microwave radiation for 2 hours a day for 45 days, they displayed cell death and shrinkage in the tubules that produce sperm. There were breaks in DNA and the formation of deformed nuclei. Testosterone levels were significantly decreased, as well as a shrinkage in testicular size. All of these changes led researchers to conclude:

"10 GHz [10,000 MHz] field has an injurious effect on fertility potential of male-exposed animals."[246]

EMF – Affect on Pregnancy
Many processes throughout pregnancy are disrupted by EMF, as a result, successful pregnancies and normal fetal development are jeopardized by EMF exposure. Melatonin is not just involved in our ability to sleep, it is intricately involved in protecting cells from oxidative stress. In the reproduction process it assists in fertilization, as well as protecting the fetus, placenta and maternal tissues throughout the pregnancy.[247] Just this one outcome of EMF radiation, decreased melatonin levels, shows that EMF exposures are capable of creating many disruptions in the normal fertilization and pregnancy processes.

In order to investigate the possible effects of radio frequency (RF) radiation on fertility, researchers placed pairs of mice at varying distances from an EMF emitting "antenna park" that contained multiple antennas. The pairs of mice were repeatedly mated five times. They found there was a progressive decrease in the number of newborns per liter, and also identified that the mice eventually became infertile due to the continuous exposure. To determine whether the infertility was reversible, they moved the mice to a place where there was no EMF radiation and found that the mice were unable to regain their fertility.[248]

A 2012 review of studies looking at EMF affect on reproduction identified that the effects differ according to the frequency, wave, strength, and duration of exposure. (This helps confirm why there are so many conflicting results from studies.) They found the impacts at the cellular level were caused by an increase in free radicals, which could decrease cell growth, create malfunctions in proteins, and result in breaks in DNA.[249]

Warning

Potential Health Effects – reproductive tract:

Infertility

EMF – Affect on Embryo Implantation

In the developing human fetus important junctions are created by trophoblast cells (the cells that play a crucial role in

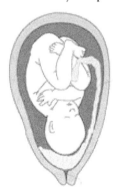 the implantation of the embryo and become the placenta). The trophoblast cell functions are influenced by connexins. The connexins and gap junctions are critically important for the close interaction that is necessary for the successful implantation of an embryo.[250]

Researchers exposing trophoblast cells to *pulsed* 1817 MHz radiation found there was a sharp decrease in the cell-to-cell gap junction-like structures. This reveals that the EMF can modify the connexin genes and proteins, as well as the very structure of the cell itself.[251]

These types of alterations could disrupt the normal functioning of trophoblast cells, resulting in difficulties for successful embryo implantation.

Warning

Potential Health Effects – on embryo implantation:

Miscarriages

EMF – Affect on Fetal Development

The connexins and gap junctions are not only important during implantation, they are also crucial for normal fetal development. During brain development and its maturation, communication taking place in gap junctions aids with vital information transferring between developing nerve cells, which is in part electrically transmitted.

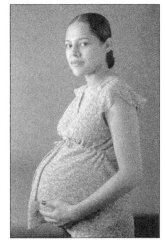

Women at 50 days pregnancy were exposed to a device emitting the cell phone frequency 900 MHz at a distance of 10 centimeters from their naval for 20 minutes. In examining the fetal tissues, researchers identified both increases and decreases in important proteins, which led them to conclude:

> "Cell phone EMF might alter the protein profile of chorionic tissue [outer membrane] of early pregnancy, during the most sensitive stage of the embryos. The exposure to EMF may cause adverse effects on cell proliferation and development of [the] nervous system in early embryos.[252]

Researchers concerned about the amount of EMF radiation exposure to the developing fetus from the use of laptop computers found that the power supply induces a strong electric current. The cell densities found in the fetus were 182 to 263% higher than the ICNIRP 98* basic restriction recommends to prevent adverse health effects. They were also 71 to 483% higher than recommended for adults. Based on these results, the investigators suggested that:

> "Laptop is paradoxically an improper site for the use of a LTC [lap top computer], which consequently should be renamed to not induce customers towards an improper use."[253]

*1998 EMF Protection Guidelines recommended by International Commission of Non-Ionizing Radiation Protection

The following pictures clearly demonstrate how much damage a cell phone can create in a developing fetus. The photos below compare the uteruses of 2 rats. The photo on the left is the uterus of a rat that was not exposed to cell phones, while the photo on the right is the uterus of a rat that was exposed to 2 cell phones for 30 minutes a day for 10 days.[254]

Uterus – Pregnant Rats

Unexposed:	**Exposed:**
rat uterus with 12 fetuses	to 2 cell phones for 30 minutes per day for 10 days

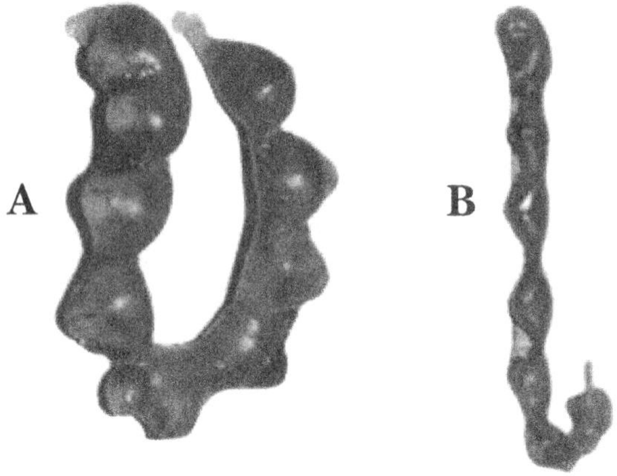

A: uterus of control rat at 20th day of gestation
B: uterus of pregnant rat exposed to EMF from 7th to 16th day of gestation

Figure 12. Exposed and unexposed pregnant rat uteruses.

Source: Ashraf El-Sayed A, Hoda S. Badr H.S., Yahia R, Salem SM, Kandil AM. Effects of thirty minute mobile phone irradiation on morphological and physiological parameters and gene expression in pregnant rats and their fetuses. *African Journal of Biotechnology.* 2011;10(84):19670-19680.
Reprinted with permission.

In picture A, 9 healthy fetuses appear to be developing within the uterus, as rats have between 6 – 24 babies per litter.

In picture B, the rat fetuses are not developing successfully.

These pictures help explain why so many women throughout the United States today are not disclosing they are pregnant until the 5th month, as they are experiencing so many miscarriages during the first 3 – 4 months of pregnancy. Researchers have identified that the oxidation damage from ROS can be responsible for these and other adverse pregnancy outcomes.[255]

Protecting the Unborn Fetus

It is incredible that the evidence of the biological harm from the microwave radiations emitted by the many wireless devices flooding the market today, and being utilized in every aspect of life, has been recognized since the beginning of their use. Barrie Trower, who was in Briton's Royal Navy and a microwave weapons specialist, has been speaking out for decades about the cellular damage these radiations create. Trower has written a very comprehensive White Paper detailing the cellular alterations created by EMF entitled: *Wi-Fi—A Thalidomide In the Making. Who Cares?* Please read his White Paper. It can be found at: http://emfsummit.com/wp-content/uploads/2014/10/WiFi-a-Thalidomide-in-the-making-who-cares.pdf.

This paper clearly identifies that fetal development is highly at risk, not only for this generation, but for generations to come. It is very confusing when so much radiation is being rolled out and only a small percentage of people have symptoms; and the health conditions that are becoming rampant are not being identified as arising from cell phone and Wi-Fi exposure. A quote from this white paper helps reveal why.

"The Reader may think that the cell phone irradiation is different from Wi-Fi as it [cell phone] has more power. In fact, Wi-Fi can be more harmful because of its lower power! Low power can enter the body and cause harm. All electromagnetic waves are accumulative. If they are below the body's threshold to cause activation of the necessary proteins required to defend and repair tissues, the damage accumulates very slowly and is undetectable like a cancer. Think of sunbathing on a cloudy day, you can still burn your skin."[256]

Again, one reason for the increased fetal development risk is that EMF can alter the connexin gap junctions that are involved in the passive transport of chemicals, which allows them to enter the placenta. The placenta is wonderfully designed to protect the fetus from toxins during its delicate development process, as the fetus does not have its own defense systems. This altering of cellular communication at the cellular level in the placenta makes it also important to explore a possible EMF connection to the epidemic in the incidence of autism, which could result from mothers absorbing sunscreens and other endocrine disruptive chemicals through their skin that could pass into the fetus due to the disruption of the placental gap junctions during its development.

New Voice Publications book: *Sunscreens – Biohazard: Treat As Hazardous Waste* describes that sunscreens are potent anti-testosterones, which would result in young developing males being more impacted compared to females. Autism statistics show that the gender ratio of autism is 5 boys affected to every 1 girl, which suggests it may be the anti-testosterone affect of sunscreen chemicals could be one of the factors as to why more boys are diagnosed with autism. For more details, see the additional information provided at: www.SunscreensBiohazard.com.

EMF – Affect on Immature versus Mature Cells

When rats were exposed to 1.8 GHz (1800 MHz) EMF for 2 hours a day for 45 days, researchers found the DNA damage was greater in immature rats, and the damage did not repair compared to the more mature rats, they concluded:

"Because much higher and irreversible cytogenotoxic [cellular DNA toxin] damage was observed in immature rats than in mature rats, further studies are needed to understand effects of EMF on DNA damage and DNA repair, and to determine safe limits for [the] environment and human[s], especially for children."[257]

Researchers subjected immature (2 weeks old) and mature (10 weeks old) rats to 900 MHz electromagnetic field (EMF) for 2 hours a day for 45 days and investigated changes in the antioxidant systems in the lymphoid organs, the spleen, thymus, bone marrow, white blood cells and plasma. They identified that EMF exposure resulted in substantial, deleterious biochemical changes in oxidative stress metabolism. Examining them after 15 days, the rats only showed limited recovery from the damage, especially in immature rats. The researchers also concluded: "In the present study, much higher levels of irreversible oxidative damage were observed in the major lymphoid organs of immature rats than in mature rats."[258]

Focusing on the effects of the common cell phone frequency of 900 MHz RF–EMF, researchers exposed immature and mature rats for 2 hours a day for 45 days with SAR values in the range of 0.38 – 0.78 W/kg. The cytogenotoxic DNA damage in immature rats was statistically higher than the mature rats and 15 days provided for a recovery period did not reduce the damage to the same extent as the control groups. Seeing the greater irreversible damage in immature rats compared to mature rats, the researchers concluded: "More sensitive studies are required to elucidate the possible carcinogenic risk (cancer creating) of EMF exposure in humans, especially children."[259]

These studies show us that our children's immature cells are much more susceptible to damage and are less able to repair the damage from EMF exposure.

Warning

Potential Health Effects – on developing mammals:

Birth defects
DNA defects

EMF – Affect on Asthma Incidence in Children

Kaiser Hospital in Northern California followed 626 children for up to 13 years after birth. Their mothers carried meters for 24 hours during the first trimester of the pregnancy to measure the magnetic field (MF) levels they received. The researchers found an increased risk of asthma with increased EMF exposure, and reported that the EMF radiation during pregnancy directly correlates to asthma at 12 years of age.

> "Our findings provide new epidemiological evidence that high maternal MF levels in pregnancy may increase the risk of asthma in offspring."[260]

This study identifies that the increase in EMF radiation could be one reason why there is such an increased incidence of asthma in children. Compound this with the blood cells not being able to carry their full supply of oxygen to the lungs, children with asthma are at a great disadvantage.

Warning

Potential Health Effects – on fetal development:

Increased asthma incidence in children

EMF – Affect on Obesity Incidence in Children

In another published study, Kaiser Hospital in Northern California followed 733 children for up to 13 years after measuring the magnetic field (MF) levels of the mothers during their pregnancy. The mothers carried a meter for 24 hours measuring their milliGauss (mG–thousandth of a gauss–a measure of the magnetic field) levels during the first trimester of pregnancy. They found the higher the radiation dose, the greater association with persistent obesity in their children.

EMF Radiation Exposure and Obesity

Levels of Radiation Exposure

	≤1.5 mG	1.5-2.5 mG	>2.5 mG
Obesity increase		1.85 OR*	2.80 OR*

* OR=odds ratio=probability an outcome will occur from a given exposure.

Source: Li DK, Ferber JR, Odouli R, Quesenberry CP Jr. A prospective study of in-utero exposure to magnetic fields and the risk of childhood obesity. *Sci Rep.* 2012;2:540.

The EMF radiation exposure during pregnancy directly correlated to obesity at 12 years, with an increased risk of 85% for 1.5 – 2.5 mG exposure and 180% for a greater than 2.0 mG exposure that a child exposed to radiation during the first trimester of pregnancy will be obese. They concluded that:

> "Maternal exposure to high MF during pregnancy may be a new and previously unknown factor contributing to the worldwide epidemic of childhood obesity/overweight."[261]

This study indicates the proliferation of EMF radiation coming from wireless technologies, which have saturated the globe, bombarding the pregnant woman and the fetus can be a very important contribution to the present epidemic of obesity.

Warning

Potential Health Effects – on fetal development:

Increased obesity incidence in children

These studies highlight the need of protecting the ovaries and eggs of young women, the fetuses of pregnant mothers, and the rapidly developing brains of young children from EMF radiation. Considering the possibility of fetal cell disruption, we strongly suggest minimizing all EMF exposure before and during pregnancy. This would include cell phones, tablets, laptops and microwave ovens. Erring on the side of caution by protecting pregnant women from EMF radiation is crucial while researching EMF emissions altering important pathways that can result in damage to the eggs and abnormal fetal development.

EMF – Affect on Children and Teenagers

In Taiwan in 2009, a nationwide study of mobile phone use in 11 – 15 year olds in relation to health symptoms was conducted among 2,042 children. They found 63% reported having used a mobile phone in the past month, and that use was associated with significant increases in headaches and migraines, as well as significant increases in itchy skin. In addition, the health status of the mobile phone users was considered worse than it was in the previous year. The researchers concluded that: ". . . our study tended to suggest a need for more cautious use of mobile phones in children, because children are expected to experience a longer lifetime exposure to radiofrequency electromagnetic fields (RF–EMF) from mobile phones."[262]

Leukemia

It is difficult to design studies to determine the effect of EMR on childhood leukemia. However, in 2010 after reviewing studies published between 1979 and 2008 on the association between environmental exposure to non-ionizing radiation and the risk of childhood leukemia, the researchers concluded:

> "In summary, the epidemiological evidence reviewed in this article reveals a consistent pattern of increased leukemia incidence in children exposed to low electromagnetic fields."

> "There appears to be an urgent need to reconsider exposure limits for low frequency and static magnetic fields, based on combined experimental and epidemiological research into the relationship between exposure to non-ionizing radiation and adverse human health effects."[263]

EMF – Impact on Children's and Teenagers' Brains

Children's heads are more susceptible to EMF because their skulls are still developing (soft) and smaller. The images below show the deeper penetration of EMF into children's brains.

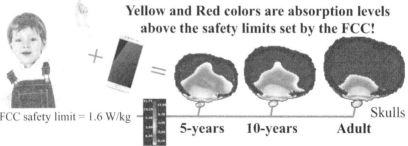

Yellow and Red colors are absorption levels above the safety limits set by the FCC!

FCC safety limit = 1.6 W/kg

5-years   10-years   Adult   Skulls

Many countries recommend limited or **no cell phone use** for children!

Source: Gandhi OP, Morgan LL, de Salles AA, Han YY, Herberman RB, Davis DL. **Exposure limits: the underestimation of absorbed cell phone radiation, especially in children.** *Electromagn Biol Med.* 2012;31(1):34-51. Creative Commons—Reprinted in Research Gate.

The Danger to Our Youth – Brain Damage

In the *Environmental Health Perspectives* article, which identified leakage in the blood-brain barrier and damage to nerve cells discussed earlier in Chapter 5, the researchers stated that:

"We chose 12 – 26 week-old rats because they are comparable with human teenagers—notably frequent users of mobile phones—with respect to age. The situation of the growing brain might deserve special concern from society because biologic and maturational processes are particularly vulnerable during the growth process. The intense use of mobile phones by youngsters is a serious consideration. A neuronal damage of the kind described here may not have immediately demonstrable consequences, even if repeated. In the long run, however, it may result in reduced brain reserve capacity that might be unveiled by other later neuronal disease or even the wear and tear of aging. We cannot exclude that after some decades of (often) daily use, a whole generation of users may suffer negative effects, perhaps as early as in middle age."[264]

Researchers in 2009 urged that the affect of cell phones on teenager's brains needs to be explored more. This recommendation arose when they found that rats exposed to chronic EMF cell phone frequency of 900 MHz for 1 hour a day for 28 days underwent a significant reduction in the number of cells in the hippocampus of the brain.[265]

Results of a 2012 study identified that cell phone radiation may be harmful to young developing brains. Exposing the developing rat brain to 9.9 GHz (9900 MHz) for 2 hours a day for 35 days researchers found significant changes in enzymes related to growth. They concluded that the enzymes were so crucially important that:

"Since these enzymes are related to growth, any alteration may lead to affect functioning of the brain and its development."[266]

Brain Damage

A study published in 2014 confirmed these findings. Rats divided into young and old groups were subjected to GSM cell phone microwaves for 2 hours a day for 60 days at 1.13 W/kg SAR. The brains showed oxidation stress, reduced antioxidant capacity, and increased tumor necrosis factor. The young rats' brain weights were impacted, and showed nerve damage microscopically. They concluded the article with: "The study highlights the detrimental effects of mobile phone radiations on the brain during young and adult ages. The interaction of these radiations with brain is via dissipating its antioxidant status and/ or triggering apoptotic [programmed] cell death."[267]

Warning

Potential Health Effects – enzymes altered; nerve cell damage:

Disrupted brain growth

Brain Cancer Risk

When human brain cancer cells are exposed to 9.6 GHz (9600 MHz) for 24 hours they undergo significant increases in cell division.[268] These findings are disturbing with the explosive expansion of mobile phone use throughout the world, accompanied with increased use by children, when a 2011 study stated:

". . . only one study on mobile phone use in children and adolescents and brain tumor risk has been published."[269]

Also, Hardell, et al. in 2012 (in the section on Brain Tumors) found one of the highest risks for brain cancer is for those whose first use of a wireless phone was before the age of 20.[270]

Current Validation of Harm

The results of the studies are beginning to be validated among our youth.   In 2014, an article in the United Kingdom's *The Guardian* reported that children can no longer build with blocks. They also quoted a teacher who "told of how pupils at his school were struggling to learn lines for a play, something which had not proved difficult in previous years."[271] The studies presented in this book identify children who are now immersed in wireless EMF radiations can be subjected to both of these outcomes, lack of fine motor coordination and loss of memory.

As teens and children are using cell phones and tablets more and more, these findings should be of great concern. The studies that continue to identify the possibility of damage to developing brains need to be heeded before the damage becomes apparent in more of our children. It may take 10 years or more to show up, then it may be too late to repair the brain damage that is developing every day with Wi-Fi surrounding our children no matter where they go, including all day in the classrooms, and with cell phones being used extensively by pregnant mothers, children, and young adults.

Children being in constant contact with their friends and sleeping with their phones and tablets should be reconsidered as the evidence clearly is showing the harm that can arise. In the meantime it is important to heed the words of researchers who stated:

"It is the need of the hour to teach young people to be structured, to know when to have the cell phone on, and to avoid becoming the slave of technology instead of its mastery."[272]

Chapter 13

Autism Behavior Disorders

EMF – Connection to the Autism Epidemic

"Autism spectrum disorders (ASD) are a group of developmental  disorders characterized by social and emotional deficits, language impairments and stereotyped behaviors that manifest in early postnatal life."[273]

The incidence rate of autism is growing at an exponential rate, as it was 1 in 2,222 in 1970 and increased to 1 in 58 boys by 2007. It has kept climbing as shown by the 2010 statistics that reveal the overall incidence of 1 in 68 children being diagnosed with autism. By 2018 the CDC reports 1 in 44.[274]

	All ages **2009**	Age 8 **2010**	Age 8 **2018**[274]
Boys	1 in 58	1 in 42	1 in 27
Girls		1 in 189	1 in 116
Boys and girls	1 in 100	1 in 68	1 in 44
Ratio boys to girls	4 to 1		4 to 1

Detailed throughout this book are several significant changes EMF create in the body that urgently require investigating EMF radiations and their possible link to the rapid increase.

EMF are suspect because autistic children display:
1. Abnormal cerebellum functioning
2. Decreased GABA functioning
3. Altered calcium metabolism and balance
4. Leaky gut syndrome
5. Increased gliosis and GFAP levels

EMF – Affect on Brain

With so many studies identifying that EMF result in brain cell death in every region of the brain that has been studied, EMF radiations creating brain cell death need to be included when looking at causes of the rapid epidemic rise in the incidence of autism since the 1970s.

Looking at the amount of grey matter in the brains of over 500 people diagnosed with autism spectrum disorder between 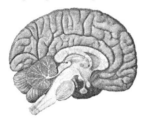 the ages of 7 to 64, researchers identified decreased grey matter in the thalamus to the cerebellum, anterior medial temporal lobes, and orbitofrontal regions of the brain. Those with a greater severity of autism had decreased grey matter volumes in the prefrontal cortex, inferior parietal and temporal regions, and temporal poles.[275] (For details see Parts of the Brain Scientists Have Identified as Being Damaged by EMF Radiation in Chapter 6).

The regions of the brain that are identified in the study above are critical areas. The cerebellum, prefrontal cortex, and temporal regions all show cellular death due to EMF radiation. Not discussed earlier in the book are the orbitofrontal and the inferior parietal regions of the brain. Even though there are no available studies identifying that EMF radiation kills cells in these regions, it would be prudent to determine whether it occurs, since autistic children exhibit damage in these areas, and display the difficulties that can arise due to damage to these sections of the brain.

The orbitofrontal is involved in the mental processing of decision making. The inferior parietal is involved in the ability to orient oneself to their surroundings. Impairment in the area results in the inability of a person to recognize mental illnesses such as depression, bipolar disorder, schizophrenia, or anxiety within themselves.[276] It also results in the inability to carry out purposeful motor movements, which includes the ability to speak, a major symptom of autism is difficulty in developing language skills.[277]

EMF – Behavior Changes from the Brain

Rats were chronically exposed to 900 MHz mobile phones *pulsed* irradiation for 6 hours a day throughout their fetal development. The hippocampus pyramidal cells showed a decrease in neuronal excitability, and phone exposure significantly altered learning acquisition and memory retention skills in male and female rats. The researchers concluded: "Our results suggest that exposure to mobile phones adversely affects the cognitive performance of both female and male offspring rats using behavioral and electrophysiological techniques."[278]

Looking at potential effects of mobile phone radiation on the central nervous system, researchers exposing 60 day old rats to a Global System for Mobile (GSM) cell phone of 1.8 GHz for 3 days identified changes in stress behavior actions in the rats.[279] Other researchers exposed rats to an active GSM 900 MHz mobile phone for 28 days and identified that there was decreased rearing and grooming frequency, which indicates that mobile phone radiation could affect the emotionality of rats.[280]

Hippocampus Behavior Changes

In another study, rats were exposed to a GSM mobile phone 900 MHz and 1.8 GHz in vibratory mode (no ring tone) to 50 missed calls for 1 hour a day for 4 weeks. They exhibited significantly altered passive avoidance behavior and changes to the structure of the cells in the hippocampus.[281]

Scientists looking at the effects of 900 MHz radio-frequency electromagnetic radiation (RF–EMR) found chemical changes that indicate oxidation activity in the amygdala, hippocampus, frontal cortex, and cerebellum regions of the brain in adolescent rats. They exposed 6 - 8 week old rats for 1 hour a day for 4 weeks to a 900 MHz GSM mobile phone kept in silent mode only (no ring tone and no vibration). At day 29, the rats showed deficits in behavioral performances. Brain cells showed that the oxidative stress was changed in the different regions of brain they examined. The researchers felt the oxidation stress could be one of the causes of the behavioral deficits that the rats exhibited after the RF–EMR exposure.[282]

Autism Changes

1. Abnormal Cerebellum Functioning

Many studies are revealing autistic children have definite alterations in their brains. EMF become suspect since the radiations have been recognized as causing:

A. Decreased cells in cerebellum
B. Deceased function of cerebellum cells
C. Reduced GABA functioning

Researchers looked at electromagnetic field (EMF) radiations effect on offspring by exposing pregnant rats to 900-MHz pulse-EMF irradiation for 6 hours a day during the whole gestation period. There was decreased neuronal excitability of Purkinje cells in rats exposed to EMF, leading the researchers to conclude:

> "In conclusion, the results of the present study show that prenatal EMF exposure results in altered electrophysiological properties of Purkinje neurons. However, these changes may not be severe enough to alter the cerebellum-dependent functional tasks."[283]

Based on findings like these, it is critically important to pay attention to a consensus published in 2012 in the medical journal *Cerebellum*. It heralded the significant advancement of scientific knowledge identifying abnormal cerebellum functioning as having a role in both the cause and development of autism. They stated studies are revealing that autistic children have defects in the function of the cerebellum, neurotransmitter deficiencies including GABA, and oxidative stress, and pointed out the cerebellum is involved with motor control and cognition, and that autistic children have problems in these areas.[284]

It may take years to identify all the alterations in behavior from decreased excitability of Purkinje cells. Just knowing that functions of these critically important cells are altered should be enough to start to implement steps that will protect unborn fetuses from EMF.

2. Decreased GABA Functioning

As just shown, autistic children are identified as having reduced GABA, which is the brain's primary neurotransmitter that calms excitatory impulses. Pyramidal cells in the hippocampus are one of the cells that secrete it. Images of the brains of children with autism spectrum disorders reveal irregularities in the medial temporal lobes and hippocampus, changes that were identified as having occurred during their development.[285]

EMF – Prenatal Cell Loss in the Hippocampus

Researchers exposing rats to cell phone radiation during gestation found decreased cells in the hippocampus in one study, and in another they identified a significant reduction in the number of pyramidal cells in the hippocampus.[286] Loss of these cells would result in decreased GABA.

Many chemicals work in the body by having a receptor on the cells they need to attach to in order to perform their functions. Without the receptor, there is no place for the chemical to land. EMF not only reduce the cells that produce GABA, this also reduces the number of receptors for the neurotransmitter GABA, and therefore impair the ability of the GABA that is available to perform its function of calming excitatory impulses. This becomes an important connection to autism as researchers are finding that impairment of GABA functioning may alter brain circuits that are responsible for emotional, communication, and social impairments—all areas that appear to be part of the core of autistic spectrum behaviors.[287]

Autistic behavior disorders are connected to hippocampus cell loss. Not only is the hippocampus involved in memory making (as discussed in the section on Alzheimer's), it is central in furnishing information that is context-specific, which frames the emotional interpretation of a specific stimulus (providing the ability to have an emotionally appropriate response to the surroundings).[288] This is important to consider as one problem autistic children have is the inability to frame their environment in a context that allows them to function in a manner that does not result in out-of-control behaviors, which can be typical of autistic children.

The link between autism and decreased GABA and its function is strengthened by the fact that a study treating autistic children with a drug that increases GABA has shown success in helping reduce their autistic behaviors.[289]

Warning
Potential Health Effects – on hippocampus prenatally and postnatally:
Autism

Autism and Seizures

Approximately 25% of autistic children have difficulties with seizures. Scientists looking at the fact that autism is often accompanied with seizures found autistic children do have a reduction in GABA receptors in the cerebellum. Based on this they concluded:

"Decreases in GABA(B) receptor subunits may help explain the presence of seizures that are often comorbid [occur together] with autism, as well as cognitive difficulties prevalent in autism."[290]

In investigating epileptic rats, researchers found a decrease in the number GABA receptors in the hippocampus. They concluded:

"Our results suggest that decreased GABA receptors in the hippocampus have an important role in epilepsy associated behavioral deficit . . ."[291]

EMF radiation becomes suspect because EMF exposure reduces the number of cells in the cerebellum and the hippocampus, creating a reduction in GABA producing cells.

Warning

Potential Health Effects – reduced GABA receptors in the
cerebellum and hippocampus:

Autism – seizures

---

3. Altered Calcium Metabolism and Balance

As stated in chapter 1, EMF activate VGCC (voltage gated calcium channels), which then alter the calcium balance between the inside and outside the cell. Research has shown one of the differences in autistic children is changes in calcium regulation (signaling) leading to impaired nerve cell function.[292]

Investigators have identified the importance of calcium balance for the integrity of the blood-brain barrier, where calcium acts as a buffer, a function that is particularly important in early brain development. They urge further exploration into the possible connection between abnormalities in these areas and autism spectrum disorders, mental retardation, ADHD, and pervasive developmental disorder, in addition to other chronic psychiatric disorders.[293]

In 2010, researchers looking at autistic brains during autopsy found they exhibit changes that include increased calcium levels, which are responsible for increases in energy metabolism and oxidative stress. They concluded that:

".. . altered [calcium balance] plays a key interactive role in the cascade of signaling events leading to autism . . ."[294]

These results are confirmed in a 2011 study that stated:

"Recent evidence has unveiled an important role for calcium signaling in the pathogenesis [development] of ASD [autism spectrum disorders]."[295]

Others have identified that defects in calcium channel genes, thereby affecting calcium balance, appear to be associated with autism spectrum disorders. These results help confirm calcium imbalance plays a role in ASD.

Based on these findings, the impact of EMF on calcium balance could be a contributing factor to the epidemic of autism.

Warning

Potential Health Effects – on calcium balance:

Autism

Autism and Cell Phones

EMF radiation creates the same biochemical changes that are being identified in our autistic children. This should herald the dire need to take immediate action to protect children from EMF radiations while research is conducted to determine whether the radiations are one of the primary causes of the increase in autism. EMF radiations become highly suspect as the exponential increase in the incidence of autism, which has been seen over the last 30 years, is the same time frame that cell phones have been introduced and rapidly proliferated around the globe.

The graph below on the left shows the increase in the number of U.S. cell phone subscribers from 1991 to 2003. The rate of increase closely matches the increasing incidence in autism over the same years as shown in the graph on the right.

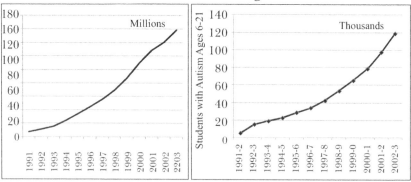

Figure 13. Number of cell phone subscribers compared to the rise of the incidence in autism.

Sources: Infoplease website. Cell Phone Subscribers in the U.S., 1985–2010. retrieved June 7, 2015 from: www.infoplease.com/ipa/A0933563.html (source: CTIA—The Wireless Association).

Yazbak FE. Autism in the United States: A Perspective. *J Amer Phys Surg*. 2003. 8(4):103-107. Reprinted with permission.

4. Leaky Gut / Digestive Problems

Autistic children have been identified as having problems with their digestive system from their esophagus to their colon, which includes increased intestinal permeability (leaky gut). Research has shown that food particles allowed to pass into the blood have the ability to influence the brain.[296]

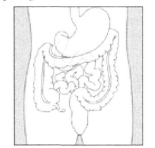

In 2004, researchers identified that some autistic children have inflamed gastrointestinal tracts (GI).[297] Published in 2009, a review of the literature further identified that autistic children have symptoms that include constipation, diarrhea, abdominal distension, increased intestinal permeability, bacterial overgrowth, and food intolerances (including milk and wheat). They also recognized that dietary changes influence autistic children's behavior, which indicates a connection between the GI tract and the central nervous system.[298]

As discussed in the section: EMF – Affect on Leaky Gut / Digestive Problems, EMF radiations impair the tight junction cells that maintain the solid integrity of the intestinal lining. When this is impaired, food particles leak into the blood stream and can create the conditions that are identified in autistic children.

Warning

Potential Health Effects – impact on intestinal lining creating leaky gut:

Autism
Autism symptoms
Autism behavioral problems
Food allergies

---

5. Increased Gliosis and GFAP Levels

Discussed in Chapter 6 in the section on EMF – Cell Death in the Brain, research was presented that shows radiation from cell phones leads to nerve cell death and scaring in the area of the cell death, which is called astrocytosis or gliosis. Researchers use glial fibrillary acidic protein (GFAP) to measure the amount of cell death. A 1993 study found that autistic children had 3 times higher GFAP in their cerebral spinal fluid than that found in a control group. This finding led the researchers to state that their results indicate that the occurrence of gliosis could result in brain damage in these children.[299]

In 2005, elevated levels of GFAP were found in several areas of the brain in autistic children making the researchers conclude that the activation of micro-, or astroglial cells indicates gliosis, which could lead to brain injury and altered developmental nerve migration.[300]

Researchers in 2011 connected the microglial activation to the underconnectivity that is seen in the brains of those diagnosed with autism spectrum disorders. In 2013, Dr. Martha Herbert, a pediatric neurologist, and Cindy Sage, an environmental consultant, published a comprehensive overview of the biochemical alterations that autistic children display that are identified as being created by EMF radiation, which included GFAP and increased glial reactivity.[301]

Since cell phone radiations are known to cause increased gliosis and increased levels of GFAP, these indicators identify that one source of the biochemical alterations observed in the brains of those with autism could be the result of EMF radiations.

Summary

There are now multiple studies published over the last few decades that identify several important biochemical changes that occur upon exposure to EMF radiations from cell phones. Since these same biochemical alterations are also being seen in autistic children, we wholeheartedly agree with the many EMF researchers like Herbert and Sage that are stating it is time to take action regarding the research that links radiations, such as those coming from cell phones, to not only the epidemic of autism, but also to the many diseases that are increasing around the world.

Chapter 14

EMF and Suicide

Teenage Suicides

As we came to a close on the final edit of this 3rd edition, we were sent a UK newspaper article (*Cotswolds Journal*) telling how Jennifer Fry's cries for help due to electromagnetic exposure from the school's Wi-Fi were ignored.[302] Ignored to the point that she felt so tormented that there was no place to go for relief, she choose to leave the planet. A tragic loss for her parents, Charles Newman and Debra Fry, as well as for her friends, classmates, and our society.

Jennifer was one of the electromagnetic sensitive people that was bothered by Wi-Fi. She and her parents complained to school officials to no avail. Their answer was that there are as many studies that say it is not harmful as there are that do. Rather than look at the hundreds of studies that raise concern, many schools and businesses choose to decide on the side that there is not enough evidence of harm. This answer led to the loss of this conscientious student, who struggled with her school work due to her Wi-Fi radiation sensitivity.

Articles were written that she was mourning the loss of a classmate who had committed suicide. Yet, increased suicides among teenagers has led the *The Atlantic* to have the cover of their December 2015 issue highlight concern of this with their article titled: "The Silicon Valley Suicides: Why Are So Many Kids with Bright Prospects Killing Themselves in Palo Alto?"[303] The article discusses the pressure to perform that these kids may be experiencing as a possible reason. However, it is important to look at the scientific studies that identify exposure to electro-magnetic radiation can increase depression and increased risk of suicide. Jennifer's school had Wi-Fi. Silicon Valley, like so many metropolitan areas today, has a very high density of electromag-netic radiation.

Decreased Melatonin and Insomnia

In 2000, *ABC Online* had an article titled: "Suicides Linked to Electromagnetic Radiation."[304] They were quoting from an article published in *The Western Journal of Medicine* by researchers looking at exposure to electromagnetic fields and suicide among electric utility workers. The researchers hypothesized that the decreased melatonin the EMF creates could result in depression and suicide.[305]

A 1988 study identified that chronic exposure to normal household 50-60 Hz (ELF) electric fields disrupts the circadian rhythm of melatonin that may contribute to depressive symptoms, and could ". . . indicate a possible sensitivity of the nervous system to ELF fields."[306] The studies in this book identify that cell phone radiations lower melatonin, which reduces deep reparative sleep. Many published studies have established a common link that insomnia and sleep disturbances are risk factors for suicide.[307]

Decreased and Altered GABA Function

There are also studies that have found a connection between decreased GABA and altered GABA function as a central and causal role for depression and in major depressive disorder.[308] Additionally, GABA levels are lowest in the most depressed patients.[309] A 2015 article published in the *Journal of Chemical Neuroanatomy* identified that reduced and altered GABA function is found in suicide cases, and EMF radiation lowers GABA and disrupts its function.[310]

Cell Phone and Computer Use Linked to Depression

In addition to the melatonin and GABA alterations being associated with increased risk for suicide, researchers have also found the exposure to the radiations of cell phones and computer use to be associated with disrupted sleep and depression. A study published in 2011 found high frequency cell phone use was a risk factor for stress, sleep disturbances, and symptoms of depression in young adults aged 20 – 24.[311] A year later, in 2012, the same researchers studying over 4,000 20 – 24 year old participants found that for men general computer use was associated with stress, sleep disturbances, and reduced performance. For women, they found using a computer without breaks was a risk factor for depression.[312]

For those who have no symptoms, unless you have been there yourself, it is impossible to relate to the 24/7 suffering EHS sensitive people are enduring. We have received many calls from people who relay:

"I have not slept in months."
"My skin itches incessantly."
"I feel constant pressure on my head."
"I do not know what to do anymore."
"There is no where I can go to feel relief from the headaches."

They continue listing the many symptoms that EMF sensitivity can create. We have heard from countless numbers of men and women who tell us their spouses, families, and medical doctors do not understand, recognize, or acknowledge the possibility that they are being impacted by EMF radiation. After speaking with us and determining they are not crazy and there are biochemical explanations for their symptoms, and that they are not the only ones who are suffering, many cry and thank us for validating their symptoms, as no one has acknowledged or understood what they are experiencing. We offer them solutions that bring these people relief within hours, leading them to call back to say: "I feel great, now!"

How many will have destroyed families and jobs, or choose Jennifer Fry's solution before the world acknowledges that there are enough studies and researchers ringing the warning bells for us on this planet to wake up, and take action before we lose its most valuable resource—its children? May we reverse the trend of ever increasing radiation sources and stop the harm that Wi-Fi radiations in schools are creating so that the children of our future do not feel as Jenny Fry did in her final words:

"I have no hope for humanity. We are destroying this beautiful earth as we speak. I am not good enough with words to stand out from the crowd and somehow help humanity. I am insignificant, an insignificant number on someone's screen and so is my whole life: a tiny blip in the whole existence of the universe, and I find it hard to be hopeful when I can barely enjoy anything anymore..........."[313]

Our hearts go out to Charles and Debra as they try to bring awareness to school boards that Wi-Fi in our schools affects children's brains and our future generations are being impacted. They do not want any other families to experience the pain they have and are going through. Our prayers go out to Jennifer's family, classmates, all the families who have suffered from teenage suicide, and to everyone who is being impacted by wireless technologies. May common sense prevail that we are electromagnetic beings not meant to be radiated by an infinite number of man-made radiation frequencies 24 hours a day, leaving no opportunity for the body to repair the damage created by EMF radiation, which it is beautifully designed to do, and can, when the radiation is removed.

Jennifer Fry
October 3, 1999 - June 11, 2015

Summary

This generation of children has been exposed to levels of EMF radiation that are unequaled throughout the history of mankind. They have become part of an unauthorized planetary experiment without their consent. The children today are exposed to 100s of frequencies of electromagnetic radiation from the time they were conceived (and even prior). Their exposure is far beyond anything that humans have been exposed to throughout our entire existence on the planet. No matter where they go, there are wireless devices and Wi-Fi radiations and electric transportation in the form of cars and trains. Thinking we cannot live without these devices, or electrifying everything to save the planet has to change, because in reality: Can we electromagnetic beings or all life forms of the planet live being bombarded with innumerable man-made electromagnetic radiations? The answer that is beginning to take shape is:

"NO!"

Chapter 15

The Planetary Unauthorized Experiment

The Precautionary Principle

When electricity was invented, there were no scientific studies conducted to see what effect it would have on living tissues. Thomas Edison received his patent for the electric light bulb in 1880, and the electrical lighting of America started in the late 1880s. It has only been in the last half of the 20th century, almost 100 years later, that proof of the harm has come to light. There is no doubt that exposure to electricity increases the risk of cancers, Alzheimer's, Parkinson's, and ALS. Even though research in the 1970s and 1980s revealed wireless technologies have the potential of causing cancers, there has been a rapid spread of them as the evidence was not heeded. Now with the overwhelming evidence presented throughout this book proving the many health problems from electrical exposure, it is imperative we begin to heed the warning words of many researchers. Two environmental researchers studying the health effects of toxins and electromagnetic radiation, Dr. Sergio Manzetti of the Fjordjorsk Marine Toxicology Department in Norway, and Dr. Olle Johansson of the Karolinska Institute in Sweden included the following comment in the conclusion of their article "Global Electromagnetic Toxicity and Frequency-induced Diseases: Theory and Short Overview" published in 2012 in *Pathophysiology*:

"From a public health point of view,
maybe it was a pity that Thomas Alva Edison
did invent the light bulb?"[314]

Dr. Samuel Milham, an epidemiology researcher, comparing the causes of death in the United States from 1920-1960 between the urban areas that had electricity to the rural areas that did not electrify in the first half of the 20th century, found an increase in what we now call the diseases of civilization including cardiovascular disease, cancer, diabetes and suicide. He came to the conclusion that these fast rising diseases and increased depression have arisen out of our adopting electrification, not by changes in lifestyle.[315]

There was no attention paid to the precautionary principle as we rapidly embraced electricity as a necessity of life, and we now have cardiovascular disease as a number one killer, with cancers number two cause of death, while suicide is the 10th leading cause of death.[316]

With this extensive presentation of the multitude of studies that identify EMF as causing biological harm, it is necessary to reemphasize what was stated in Chapter 2 regarding the need to move forward incorporating the precautionary principle in regards to EMF radiation exposure. The studies showing that EMF radiations can be harmful are so numerous that many scientists from around the world are advising that the precautionary principle should be followed with any further expansion of wireless devices.[317] With titles like the following it is clear there is an urgent need to reduce exposure while the truth of the effects of EMF radiations are still in an investigative stage.

The Electromagnetic Fields of Cellular Phones and the Health of Children and of Teenagers (the Situation Requiring to Take an Urgent Measure).[318]

Determining Health Policy for Sensible Mobile Phone Use–Current World Status.[319]

Late Lessons from Early Warnings: Towards realism and precaution with EMF?[320]

Yet, sadly, Dr. Johansson and Mats Dämvik concluded in their 2010 article "Health Risk Assessment of Electromagnetic Fields: A Conflict between the Precautionary Principle and Environmental Medicine Methodology" in *Reviews on Environmental*

Health with the statement: "Our investigation shows that the precautionary principle is not being used for its intended purpose in relation to exposure to EMF. The reason for this position is that decision-makers are being misled by inaccurate risk assessments."[321]

The studies throughout this book identify the biochemical changes that are leading to symptoms and diseases. With this health burden, we cannot afford to continue to fight over differences in interpretation of data from the available studies. Once the changes to the cells are identified, it is imperative now that we start utilizing the "Precautionary Principle" that scientists from around the world are urging us to implement due to the results of studies on EMF.

In 2005, the United Nations Educational Scientific and Cultural Organization (UNESCO) World Commission on the Ethics of Scientific Knowledge and Technology (COMEST) published a 50 page paper on the Precautionary principle. One of the definitions used was that of the European Union [EU]. In 2000, they made the statement that:

> "The precautionary principle applies where scientific evidence is insufficient, inconclusive or uncertain and preliminary scientific evaluation indicates that there are reasonable grounds for concern that the potentially dangerous effects on the environment, human, animal or plant health may be inconsistent with the high level of protection chosen by the EU."[322]

The precautionary principle is a guiding framework for decision making for actions the results of which are unknown and have not been thoroughly investigated or there is debate regarding the outcomes of the studies. It cautions that an action should not be taken if the consequences are uncertain and potentially dangerous. The burden of proof that it is "not harmful" falls on those taking the action if something has a suspected risk of causing serious harm to the public or to the environment.

The world needs to pay attention to the response of Dr. Zinelis, of the Greek Hellenic Cancer Society, to a 2010 article in *Environmental Health Perspectives* claiming the precautionary principle did not apply. In comparing where we are now in relation to EMF radiation, he brings attention to how we did not take action quickly enough in regards to asbestos. He wrote:

> "The past has taught us many lessons about risk from environmental exposures. For example, the lack of full scientific proof concerning the adverse effects of asbestos and the delay of precautionary action had devastatingly consequences to human health [World Commission on the Ethics of Scientific Knowledge and Technology (COMEST) 2005]. If asbestos had been banned in 1965, when the effects of asbestos on mesothelioma were plausible but unproven, the Netherlands alone would have saved approximately 52,000 victims and 30 billion Euro for 1969 – 2030. An estimated 250,000 – 400,000 deaths from mesothelioma, lung cancer, and asbestosis caused by past asbestos exposure will occur the next 35 years in the European Union (COMEST 2005)."

> "In conclusion, concerning the exposure to electromagnetic fields, the precautionary principle should be applied to protect humans from environmental effects of non-thermal mechanisms."[323]

Yet, the desire for everyone to be connected 24 hours a day has led to 4G wireless being beamed from "smart" light poles in Los Angeles neighborhoods, and to projects that plan on utilizing high flying stratosphere balloons to provide their customers Internet services no matter where they are in the world.[324]

Considering every man, woman, and child is exposed to EMF radiation 24 hours a day, whether they know it or not, compared to the limited exposure to asbestos, the impact on society of EMF will have incalculable numbers of people affected and costs beyond comprehension.

The Planetary Unauthorized Experiment

The mass worldwide roll out of EMF radiating devices has placed the whole planet and every living thing in the middle of the largest experiment ever conducted. The experiment was never authorized, nor were we informed or provided the opportunity to consent to participate or not. Yet, since these radiations go everywhere, no human has been offered the ability to say: "No." **There is nowhere on the planet people can go to escape as the radiations from our wireless devices, and the thousands of satellites that are beaming to us from space permeate the entire globe.** Animal advocates should be just as concerned for every living animal as they are being impacted also.

We have not had a say in our children being involved in this experiment either. Throughout America and other countries, they are being exposed to high radiation classrooms with tablets replacing books, and high powered Wi-Fi routers placed throughout the school campus to assure coverage. Studies were not performed comparing children exposed to radiation versus children in classrooms that are still provided books and encyclopedias. The studies could look at current symptoms, by comparing the number sick days and the number of visits to the nurses' office in schools with Wi-Fi and wireless services, versus schools without them. These types of epidemiological studies should have been conducted on a sample population and continued for at least 10 years (the time to development of brain tumors from cell phone use), and better yet 15 – 20 years, to determine the possible long-term effects of radiation upon children's rapidly developing bodies, especially their brains.

There are so many experiencing EHS symptoms around the world that countries have been establishing EMF Refuge Zones where people can go to live without the EMF assault of cell towers, wireless, and Wi-Fi, allowing their bodies to rest and recover. These countries include the United States, France, Italy, Spain, and Canada. The United States and Australia both have Radio Free Zones that have been established to protect their radio telescopes from electromagnetic radiations emanating from the many wireless devices that are now everywhere. France is planning EMF reduced "white zones" placed throughout the country where EHS people can find relief from their symptoms.

In Stockholm in May, 2006. a conference called "The Right for Persons with the Impairment Electrohypersensitivity to Live in a Fully Accessible Society" was organized by the Stockholm City municipality and the Stockholm County Council. They met to implement a measure that would make the city fully accessible for electrohypersensitivity people. The things they looked at were banning mobile phones from certain underground cars, public bus seats, and in electrosanitized hospital wards.[325]   It is imperative that all countries in the world provide places for people who have developed electrohypersensitivity to have places where they can live and work. The people seeking refuge in these towns are just the beginning of what will eventually become necessary for everyone on the planet.

Summary

In the face of the steadily mounting evidence proving that EMF radiation inflicts changes in so many essential processes in the body, we cannot afford to wait 10 to 20 years to confirm the results that have already been documented in the many studies covered throughout this text. Research will eventually prove the human body was not designed to be radiated 24 hours a day, with nowhere to escape to allow the body's natural ability to repair itself. The outcomes from this global experiment that is being conducted on us and our children may result in irreversible diseases and disabilities on a mass scale, affecting everyone throughout the world. Today, billions are accumulating levels of radiation that will result in an ever increasing percentage of the population developing electromagnetic sensitivity symptoms. As their bodies attempt to endure the assaults that EMF exposure is imposing upon them, many will eventually develop debilitating health issues.

As inhabitants of this glorious planet, we must band together and share the information in this book with everyone we know, as we all need to protect our bodies from the wireless devices that are already in place. If we do not take action now to reduce our exposure, as these technologies become more powerful and more plentiful, they will have a greater impact on our health, not only ours and our children's, but also on the generations to come.

Part 4

Solutions – Protecting Yourself and Your Family

Chapter 16

Correction and Prevention Are the Keys

Now that you understand the potential for harm that can arise from EMF exposure:

"What can you do to protect yourself and your family?"

EMF and wireless technologies surround us everywhere today. Until the information in this book becomes common knowledge, there will be no slowing of the ever increasing types and numbers of wireless devices that will further increase the density of EMF smog from which we all need to protect ourselves. Since EMF radiation is cumulative, it is necessary for everyone to reduce the amount of their daily exposure. Most of the time there are straightforward steps that everyone can take to create a vast improvement in the safety of their environments. Other times, it will take considering making more extensive changes.

It all begins with evaluating your current surroundings to determine the sources of radiation exposure. The goal is to eliminate or reduce the exposure to everything electrical in the areas where you spend the most time. The less radiation in your environment, the more your body will have an opportunity to rest, recover, and regenerate from the assault that it has to endure while being in public areas with Wi-Fi and other uncontrollable EMF exposures. We know that it will not be possible or realistic to eliminate all of today's must-have conveniences. However, it would be highly beneficial to eliminate or reduce the exposure in as many ways as you can, or are willing to give up. The more you can eliminate or protect against, the better off you and your family will be.

Body Electronics – Evaluate the Risk vs. Benefit

Smartwatches, fitness trackers, and headsets (hearing aides, earbuds, etc.) with either Wi-Fi or Bluetooth connections should be evaluated. Any time you attach or carry electronic devices on your body, they act as antennas attracting EMF energies to your body. For electronics attached to the head areas, keep in mind your brain is between the headset devices. We feel these devices are very compromising and should be avoided. As of 2023, physicians and scientists state the studies have not kept up with the rapidly escalading technologies to determine whether they are safe. Please consider whether you really, really need that new device drawing more EMF energies to your body for extended periods of exposure.

Evaluating Your Environments

Work Environments
Check with the individual in charge of your work facility to see if the company will have you location inspected for excessive EMF. Express your concern over identifying whether there are high EMF radiation spots that can be decreased or eliminated to reduce the exposure for all of its employees.

If the building has Wi-Fi, check to determine whether the wired connections are still available and have them reconnected. If not, request to have a wired system installed and eliminate the wireless Wi-Fi system.

Having work stations next to walls that have PBX phone systems, banks of computer servers, or high voltage electrical services should be avoided. If they are found to be emitting a large electrical field, move employees a safe distance away from these areas.

Steps to Protect Your Living Spaces
Limit the amount of electrical interference. The walls of buildings provide some insulation from these invisible beams of radiation. However, windows provide very little or no protection. If you have a choice to sit behind an exterior wall or look out a window, choose the wall to reduce the exposure from outside sources.

Find out what is behind the walls around you to determine whether there are sources of EMF emissions that could be impacting the area. If you determine there is an electrical power source such as a wireless device, Wi-Fi router, or smart meter move as far away from that wall as possible to protect yourself from the emissions.

Avoid electric heat. It adds to the cumulative load, and as mentioned in the section on EMF – Connection to Alzheimer's Disease, the long-term effect of electric heat increases the risk of being more likely to develop Alzheimer's disease.[326]

Bedrooms

All electrical devices emit electromagnetic radiation, so start with the basics of removing as many electrical devices as you can. It is especially important to reduce EMF while you sleep so the body can undergo repair of its cells and DNA, which is essential for us to either regain or maintain good health.

Remove computers, Wi-Fi routers, or high output electrical devices, including televisions, especially the new smart televisions from your sleeping areas. Also make sure there are no electrical devices on or near the wall where your headboard rests (such as in a room behind the wall).

Do not use your cell phone as an alarm clock or place an electric clock or radio near your head. Get a large numbered alarm clock that can be seen from a distance, or a small battery operated alarm clock.

Make sure all your electric appliances are grounded. Unplug electrical devices. Even a simple lamp cord will emit a large amount of EMF, as the cord itself emits radiation even when the device is not turned on.

Investigate the ability to turn off the circuit breakers to your sleeping area off at night. This would provide the greatest opportunity for your body to repair while you sleep.

Design your bedroom to be sanctuary:
Free from EMF!

Give your cells an opportunity to:

Rest, repair, and recover!

Grounding

Grounding naturally provides the body with the earth's electrons we no longer receive because we do not walk barefoot, and we live in houses with insulating floors. The electrons received from the earth assist in repairing the damage that occurs throughout the day, providing a greater ability to survive in this wireless age. Obtain bedding sheets or mats that allow you to stay grounded all night. Make sure they are made from natural fibers such as 100% cotton, as synthetics attract electricity.

When the body is exposed to wireless devices, the red blood cells clump together. Grounding the body provides the return of the normal electrical charge on the blood cells, which allows them to separate and go back to their normal doughnut-like shape. This can occur within 30 to 45 minutes of grounding.

Kitchens

Do not use microwave ovens. The radiation can leak through the door, and the FDA advises not to stand against or directly in front of the oven while it is operating. You will be amazed at how easily you will adjust to not using one and wonder why you felt you needed one. (You can have a hot cup of water in less than a minute from the stove top.)

Today, there are people whose electromagnetic radiation accumulation has reached their saturation point. They develop vertigo, dizziness, nausea, and other EHS symptoms when they turn on their electric stove tops.

Reduce your EMF exposure!

Cell Phones

Use cell phones, tablets, laptops, or computers as little as possible. We know how difficult this is in today's modern world, but looking at all the accumulating evidence of damage, it is not worth risking a future of suffering from a debilitating disease resulting from over exposure.

The new cell phones have GPS (global positioning system) and are designed to transmit periodically to update their location, even when turned off. The only way to ensure that this *pulsing* is not taking place is to take the battery out. If your cell phone has a removable battery, remove it when you are not using it. If you cannot take the battery out, keep it as far away from you as you can while working or sleeping. Before I strengthened my body, I could feel sharp, needlepoint pains in my legs, feet, and back from the new more powerful 3G and 4G phones transmitting even from 30 – 40 feet away.)

If your phone has a hands free speaker option, use it rather than keep your phone next to your head. There are air tube headsets that can also increase the distance from the phone.

Wireless earpieces (e.g., Bluetooth) do put out less radiation, but people wearing these devices for many hours each day are creating an antenna on the side of their heads. They still expose brain tissue to disrupted cell activity and glucose metabolism, increasing the risk of cancer in those areas. Also, when the signal is weaker due to being a greater distance from a cell tower, the cell phone has to use more power to make the connection, so attempt to use it only when it shows the strength of 4 bars of reception. Another disadvantage of wearing an earpiece is that you cannot see when your phone has to power up in areas where the reception is not as good.

Do not carry your cell phone next to your body such as in a front or rear pants pocket. Anywhere you place these devices becomes an antenna, bringing its signal to the body parts in that area. Young boys and girls who are placing cell phones in their pockets are risking difficulty with fertility. It is not worth the risk.

Women should protect their breasts and never carry their phones in their bras. Pregnant women should keep their cell phones or wireless devices away from their bodies, especially around the stomach area to protect their developing babies.

Companies are now offering home phones that come in as a wireless service and many people have given up their land line phones, resulting in using their cell phones 100% of the time. Retain or go back to a wired land line phones wherever possible. They are available and are worth the effort to seek them out.

Do not use cordless phones, as they also emit strong radiation that leads to ill effects, such as headaches, nausea, or skin itching. Many systems are stronger than cell phones, and some operate at 5.8 GHz. Steven Sinatra, M.D., co-author of *Earthing*, opens many of his presentations stating that one of the most dangerous objects in homes today are the cordless phones. He advises people to remove them immediately.

Do not exercise with your cell phone. It is amazing how people cannot provide their bodies with the benefit of jogging or working out at a gym because they carry their cell phones in their pockets and take numerous calls throughout their workouts. If they are diabetics, or one whose blood sugar is now sensitive to EMF radiation, increases in blood sugar can result in their exercise being harmful rather than beneficial.[327]

It has not been that many years since everyone functioned and thrived with only land line phone service. We did not need to be in constant contact 24 hours a day no matter where we were. It is tragic that families cannot go out into nature and just enjoy it and each other anymore. I still spend as much time as possible at the beach for grounding on the sand and am very saddened to see entire families, including their small children, walking along in the waves and around the park, each with their cell phones to their ears. They cannot be getting the full benefit of the grounding, nor are they providing emotional support for each other as a family unit. Giving up our cell phones will not only bring good health, it could also bring families closer together again.

Children's brains are more susceptible to radiation due to their smaller size, more fluid, and rapidly dividing DNA. They should not be given cell phones or tablets. We see parents placing them in front of their very young children in restaurants to act as baby sitters. This is a hazard that should be avoided as the EMF exposure these children are receiving will have an impact on their long-term future health.

It is not a toy!   **It is not a babysitter!**

Laptops, Tablets, and Computers

Do not use your laptops or tablets in your lap. Keep them as far away from your body as you can. Do not leave them in sleep or hibernation mode, rather turn them on only when you need to use them. In sleep and hibernation modes, they are still on and are emitting an electrical field. Pregnant women should keep them away from their stomach area, the same as cell phones.

Whenever possible, turn off the wireless capabilities and connect to a wired connection for Internet service. Make sure the Wi-Fi is turned off—using the hardwire connection does automatically not turn off the Wi-Fi function).

Televisions and Smart TVs

Avoid having a TV in the bedroom. If you must, consider getting one that you can unplug when not using. TVs are much more powerful than you think. My EHS symptom included my skin opening up and bleeding when the TV was turned on.

If you have an old tube television, consider getting a flat screen as they emit less energy. However, the new smart televisions emit more, and are difficult for people with EHS to be around.

Using Devices to Reduce EMF Toxicity From Electronics

There are devices available that work to reduce the EMF toxicity from electronics. With the plethora of EMF mitigating devices available, it is often difficult to select one. We found and use a product line developed in Europe that works best for us. For details see pages 229 - 234.

Home and Workspace Environments

Evaluate your electronic devices to ensure they are not emitting excessive EMF radiations. One of our computers was not grounded properly and did not have shielded electrical cords to the computer's processor and monitor. In addition, the monitor was an old cathode tube style and needed to be replaced with a newer flat screen. We discovered we were being bombarded by over 6 times what is considered safe exposure. The radiation waves coming from this one computer and monitor made it impossible to work well or efficiently. The cost to reduce the EMF exposure to what is "considered safe" at this workstation was about $120, but well worth the investment.

If you are using a wireless mouse, keyboard, printer, or router go back to wired. This is a simple, quick reduction in the amount of radiation your body is accumulating. It has become common for everyone to have their own computer, router, and printer sitting next to them, however, all of these devices are emitting EMF radiation. Move them as far away as possible to reduce your exposure. Also, most printers create a dust cloud of toxic chemicals that you do not want to breathe. Move the printers to an area that is well ventilated and seldom used.

Computer workstations generally have an excessive number of electrical cords and outlet bars that create an EMF zone. Move the power cords and outlet bars as far away from where you sit as possible.

The same grounding we recommend for your bed should be applied to your workstations. Obtain a grounding mat to place under your feet while working on your computer. If you have computers at home and at work, use this simple grounding at all workstations.

Reduce and eliminate all fluorescent lights. The light bothers many who become electromagnetic sensitive. They are capable of creating migraine headaches in sensitive people. Before I repaired and strengthened my body, due to my cumulative EMF radiation load, my skin would burn like a sunburn from my kitchen ceiling fluorescent lights, even though I had lived under them for 20 years with no burning reaction. In addition, the blue light they emit lowers melatonin, which is already being decreased by the amount of EMF radiation we are exposed to daily, leading to loss of restorative sleep.

Also, they contain the toxic heavy metal mercury, which is a health hazard, and why there are labels on the compact fluorescent bulbs warning users to do an entire hazmat clean up when they are broken due to the release of the poisonous mercury. Plus, there has been some reporting that the curly bends in the compact fluorescent bulbs allow mercury to escape. Therefore, utilize the safer incandescent bulbs wherever you can.

Utility Smart Meters

Determining Which Meter You Have

How do you know if you have an electric, gas, and water smart meter or not? If the meter has wheels and dials like a clock pointing to numbers you may still have an old safe analog mechanical meter, which you want to keep. If you have old analog meters for electric, gas and water, call your utility companies TODAY and tell them you want to be on their permanent opt-out lists to ensure that you keep your old meters. Once it has been removed, it is much harder to obtain an old analog meter.

If your meter has a digital readout on the face plate, it is a wireless EMF emitting meter. Should you determine that any of the electric, gas, or water meters are a smart meter, ask your utility companies to change it back to the safe analog type, and to be placed on their permanent opt-out lists. Check with your state to determine its policy. California ruled that smart meters could not be mandatory and customers needed to be offered their choice. This means that if a smart meter was installed, the utility company has to provide the same type of meter that was removed—a safe analog meter.

Analog Meter

Digital Smart Meter

Some new meters are being installed that do have a clock face, but inside there is a transmitter that may or may not be turned on. Check with your utility company to make sure that they have not turned on the transmitter that is within these meters.

Some electric utility companies state they do not have the analog/legacy (clock face) meters to reinstall and have been installing digital meters that can be read from the street as a meter reader drives down your street. You want to make sure your replacement is a clock face meter or a meter without a transmitter of any kind. Utility companies have installed meters without a transmitter where people have stated it is necessary for health reasons.

As of 2016, some California electric companies charge a one-time setup fee of $75 and $10 a month to keep your safe meter, and will break up the $75 fee into several payments. If you are under the low income program these fees are reduced to $10 to reinstall and $5 per month. The monthly charge of either the $10 or $5 is the best health insurance you can buy. In California, it has been ruled the utility companies can only charge the additional fees for 3 years. Hopefully, other states will adopt this ruling. (Also check your bills as there have been many reports of significant increases in monthly charges with the new meters.)

If you live in an apartment complex, check to see how close you are to the bank of meters servicing the building. Attempt to move to a building that does not have banks of meters, or a to single dwelling where you are in charge of not only the utility meters, but also your entire environment. In apartments or condominiums, it is difficult to control whether your neighbors are utilizing wireless technologies on the other side of a shared wall, but it can be done.

Protecting Your Home

Turn off and unplug as many of your electronics as you can while you are not using them, and at night when you go to bed. If you maintain a Wi-Fi router, turn it off so that your body's cells will have an opportunity to rest and repair. The more time you can give your body a break from the assault from these electromagnetic fields, the better chance you have of remaining healthy.

Now that we are surrounded in a sea of electricity, there are many who are working on even more solutions to provide safe environments where we live and work. With the rapid advances in technology that are continually being introduced, many new innovations will appear on the market. We will be continually researching them and providing information regarding their effectiveness in our newsletter: *NewsFlash*.

Moving to a New Location

When moving to a new home, apartment, or office consider what in the surrounding area may be generating an electrical field. Anytime you are going to make a long-term commitment to live or work somewhere, always verify that it is safe. Check where the power lines and cell towers are in relationship to where you will be spending your time. Many cell towers are easy to spot, however, some cell towers are hidden in enclosures. You do not want to move next to a building that has a hidden cell phone tower. A church near us erected a beautiful stained glass tower to hide the cell tower they allowed to be erected on their property. Our closest tower is located at the high school in a covered structure that makes it undetectable. New buildings are being erected with antennas hidden from view. As consumers, become informed and know what potential dangers might be hidden from the public's view.

There are services on the Internet that provide the locations of the cell towers and antennas in the area. Find out where they are and how close they are to the location you are considering before buying  or renting. Look for registered, non-registered, and proposed cell towers. A good website resource can be found at:

www.antennasearch.com

Solar Panels

Be aware of anything that will be generating an electrical field in your environment. We would not place solar panels on our roof or consider living, sleeping, or working under them. EHS sensitive people are telling us that they become sick around the solar that is in and around their living environment. The inverter unit that converts the DC current to AC current seems to bother them the most. Also, if you have solar panels, most utility companies require that they be used in conjunction with a smart meter. Therefore, a solar system creates additional EMF exposure from the panels, inverter, and smart meter energies.

**Until more research has been conducted,
we would not recommend solar.**

Transportation: Trains, Planes, and Vehicles

Public Transportation

Faraday's law identifies that EMF are reflected by metal and therefore amplified within metal containers. This means everyone utilizing public transportation is being subjected to much more radiation inside these vehicles because of the widespread use of cell phones and Wi-Fi devices by passengers. This is proven in a study conducted across five European countries. Utilizing personal exposure meters, they identified the greatest radiation that people were subjected to was while riding on public forms of transportation—trains and buses—as well as in their cars, due to use of cell phones by those on board.[328]

Electric Trains and the Environment

The environmental movement to save the planet has resulted in the creation of electric trains being installed in major cities and rapidly expanding across the  planet. Now we are hearing from electromagnetic sensitive people who state that they do not feel well while riding in the electric trains. Since the electromagnetic radiation is cumulative, the more we humans are exposed to it, the less we will be able to tolerate it or be around it. Also, all businesses and homes where the trains are running nearby are being exposed to the additional electromagnetic radiation from the power lines utilized to operate the trains.

Does it make sense to save the planet if we all become so disabled we can no longer enjoy it?

It is not just we humans who are being, affected, all life forms on the planet are being impacted by this increasing onslaught of electromagnetic radiations. Environmental policies need to include being good stewards of all species that share this precious planet with us.

Airplane Travel and Wi-Fi Access

It is important to bring attention to the amount of EMF radiation people are now exposed to when they fly. Airline attendants and pilots have looked to us for help, telling us how sick they feel at the end of every flight. This is of particular concern now that Wi-Fi is furnished on the flights, with many on board using cell phones, computers, and tablets. The airline employ-ees who have become disabled and have seen their fellow employees becoming disabled, are expressing concern over never being able to reach retirement. They are the canaries who are showing us providing Wi-Fi in flight is not worth the harm it is creating.

Flight crews and passengers are spending long periods of time traveling in a metal tube that allows the radiations to bounce around inside. It is important to look at the harm created by being able to use so many electronic devices in these confined spaces. It is advisable to rethink allowing people to use them on board flights. Additionally, there is EMF radiation from all the computers that are required to fly the plane, which are particularly excessive for the pilots in the cockpit. More radiation is also added by all the monitors throughout the plane that present the in-flight movies. This is increased by the planes that are equipped with  the monitors embedded inside the headrests of each seat. This exposure is important for everyone to remember when they are considering flying.

We have had the opportunity to help many airline employees stay on the job with using the energy optimizers. We have observed vast improvements in the health and vitality they experience once they start wearing them, as well as utilizing them on the electronics they use.

Personal Vehicles

Since cell phones create far greater radiation when used inside vehicles, limit your use in the car. Better yet, keep the battery out of all phones on board while you are driving and use them only in emergencies. Today most vehicles are setup for Bluetooth and GPS navigation systems, continuous Wi-Fi on board, as well as computers with many apps that are hard to avoid. If you have the option to go with a lower technology vehicle, do it. Commuters and those who spend a great amount of time in their

vehicles should limit their exposure by not purchasing a vehicle loaded with electronic devices (or do not activate the optional wireless services).

People who have developed EHS find they cannot drive or ride in cars with built-in wireless and GPS. Some have found when they asked the auto manufacturer to disconnect them, they were told they are so intricately embedded in the vehicle's computer system, they cannot be disabled.

The harm of EMF exposure while driving is identified by researchers who evaluated the amount of oxidation damage created by electromagnetic radiation that is created inside a car. They exposed human blood platelets to an electromagnetic field for 30 minutes in a laboratory that was designed to create the electromagnetic radiation generated by car electronics, physiotherapy equipment, and LCD monitors. They found increased oxidation from all 3 EMF radiation sources, with the most significant changes after exposure to the EMF generated by car electronics. These investigators concluded that the low frequency electromagnetic fields generated by car electronics, physiotherapy equipment, and LCD monitors may be a cause of oxidative stress in the human body and may lead to the development of diseases that arise from free radical oxidation damage.[329]

Hybrid and Electric Vehicles

Even though few studies have looked at the biological impact of riding in an electric car, based on all the evidence presented in this book, it would not make sense to place yourself or your family in the energy field of electric generating vehicles. The hybrids that use the vehicle's wheels to generate power are small generating plants, and create an electrical energy field within the vehicle. Also, solar panels are being placed on the top of cars that generate power for the vehicle's air conditioner. As discussed earlier, Faraday's law tells us that the electrical field within these types of vehicles would bounce around inside increasing the intensity. These may not be safe options to purchase.

We have identified that increasing difficulty with EHS symptoms is connected to driving an electric car. One woman who was becoming more and more disabled from EHS identified it was from driving her mother's electric car that she inherited when her mother passed away from Alzheimer's. After becoming so sick herself, she now realizes her mother, who became very nauseous when she drove her to her doctor's appointments, was sick due to the electric car. At the time, she thought her mother just did not want to see the doctor.

We are hearing from people who cannot ride in electric cars without dizziness, vertigo, and nausea. One parent told us their child cannot ride in their electric car without vomiting. Again, until more research has been conducted, we would not recommend purchasing these vehicles, especially if you are EMF sensitive, nor do you want to increase your radiation exposure, increasing your risk of becoming EHS.

Electric car

Driverless Vehicles

Since people are already becoming sick in today's version of hybrid and electric cars, it is difficult to comprehend that driverless cars are in development and will be here in the near future. The amount of radiation that will be required both inside and outside of these cars will be far greater than what some already cannot tolerate. Now is the time to look at the true impact of the freedom that is being sought to have driverless cars, and realize they will not be worth the harm they are capable of generating.

Changing Your Diet Can Strengthen Your Body

Drink Plenty of Water
Stay well hydrated – our bodies are 70 to 90% water. Providing the amount your cells need to function at their maximum efficiency will assist them in providing their maximum protection.

Antioxidants Protect the Body from EMF Damage
Research is continuing to reveal the body needs antioxidants to repair the damage from stress and toxins, and now is proving this to be true for EMF radiation as well. Antioxidants repair the damage from the free radicals and reactive oxygen species (ROS) that occur from EMF radiation exposure, the same as those generated by chemicals and solar radiation. The following are the antioxidants that research is proving protects from the oxidation damage created by EMF.

Vitamins C and E
In exposing rats to the cell phone frequency of 900 MHz, researchers identified oxidation damage in their brain tissue. One group was provided vitamin C along with the 900 MHz exposure. The vitamin C showed protective effects from the oxidation damage to the brain. Their conclusion: "Our results suggest that vitamin C may play a protective role against detrimental effects of mobile phone radiation in brain tissue."[330]

Researchers found that groups of rats that were provided vitamins C and E were capable of maintaining normal testicular tissue when exposed to 900 MHz radiation for 15, 30, and 60 minutes a day for 2 weeks. Whereas, the rats not provided these vitamins showed markers of oxidation damage to the testicles.[331]

The researchers who measured the effect of 900 MHz cell phone radiation on the uterus endometrium included looking at whether vitamins could protect against the radiation oxidation damage. They too found that the combination of vitamins C and E caused a significant decrease in this damaging effect of EMR.[332]

Caffeic Acid Phenethyl Ester (CAPE)

The researchers who identified heart tissue damage from 900 MHz mobile phone also found that caffeic acid phenethyl ester (CAPE), one of the major components of honeybee propolis (a potent free radical scavenger and antioxidant), exhibits a protective effect against the heart damage.[333]

A 2014 review focused on known kidney damaging agents and on the research that looked at the ability of caffeic acid phenethyl ester (CAPE) to protect the kidneys from the oxidative stress created by the toxic substances. CAPE was selected for these studies due to its known antioxidant, anti-inflammatory, antiproliferative, cytotoxic, antiviral, antifungal properties. The studies do show it provides a protection from the oxidative damage that occurs to the kidneys from toxic agents. Electromagnetic radiation at 900 MHz was listed among the kidney damaging agents, a list which also included immunosuppressive drugs, chemotherapy drugs, antibiotics that cause kidney damage, heavy metals like cadmium, tobacco, damaging chemicals including toluene, carbon tetrachloride, and the herbicide paraquat. The studies did verify that CAPE prevents the oxidation damage to kidney tissue from all these toxic substances, including EMF radiation.[334]

β-glucan Skin Protection

In studying rats exposed to 2.45 GHz EMR for 60 minutes a day for 4 weeks, researchers identified their skin tissues showed significant oxidation creating tissue damage. When the rats were provided the antioxidant acting β-glucan, there was a significant reversal in the oxidation markers. This shows that β-glucan's antioxidant properties could protect against the oxidative skin injury of electromagnetic radiation.[335]

Gingko Biloba

Rats exposed to 900 MHz EMR from a mobile phone for 1 hour a day for 7 days showed oxidation damage in brain tissue that was prevented by ginkgo biloba. The researchers concluded:

"Reactive oxygen species [ROS] may play a role in the mechanism that has been proposed to explain the biological side effects of MP [mobile phones], and Gb [ginkgo biloba] prevents the MP-induced oxidative stress to preserve antioxidant enzymes activity in brain tissue."[336]

Adding as many antioxidants and nutrients to your diet as you can has become essential not only to maintain health, but to repair the damage that is now going on 24 hours a day from EMF radiation. In general, because the EMF assault is so massive, the more antioxidants you consume, the more you will support good health on many levels.

Please add these antioxidants as organic. Since pesticides and EMF create more harm together, switching to organic would make sense. If you cannot afford to go 100% organic, learn the products that contain the most pesticides and avoid them. The Environmental Working Group (EWG) has a list of the Dirty Dozen Plus™, which contain more pesticides than other fruits and vegetables and should be purchased as organics when possible. They are:

1. Apples
2. Celery
3. Cherry tomatoes
4. Cucumbers
5. Grapes
6. Nectarines – imported
7. Peaches
8. Potatoes
9. Snap peas
10. Spinach
11. Strawberries
12. Sweet bell peppers

Plus:
Hot peppers
Kale / Collard greens[337]

Many antioxidant foods and supplements have been proven to offset ROS damage created by the sun. Since both EMF and sunlight create oxidative damage, the antioxidants that provide protection from solar radiation will also protect against EMF damage as well. A comprehensive list of antioxidants proven to provide solar radiation protection and the importance of combining many due to their synergistic actions is available in the book: *Sunscreens – Biohazard: Treat As Hazardous Waste*.

EMF Safety Check List
Reduce EMF Exposure: Living / Working / Public Areas

Environmental Modifications

Consider every item you bring into your living and working spaces as adding to the EMF toxic load, or contain chemicals that will outgas into your environment (e.g., furniture and floorings outgas formaldehyde).

Design your bedroom to be sanctuary: Free from EMF!

Decrease use of cell phones, computers, and wireless devices.
1. Keep cell phones away from your body (use the speaker option).
2. Take the battery out when you are not using it.
3. Go back to wired Internet and phones where possible (do not use Wi-Fi or cordless).

Remove all utility smart meters: gas, electric, and water.
1. Call your utility companies to be placed on permanent opt-out lists for the smart meters.
2. Make every effort to keep analog meters on your residence.
3. If a smart meter is already installed, exchange it for an analog meter (let them know you need it for health reasons).

Remove electrical objects from sleeping areas.
1. Clock radios (convert to a small battery one).
2. Televisions.
3. Cell phones / cordless phones.
4. Computers / laptops / tablets or Wi-Fi routers.
5. Do not use electric blankets or heating pads.
6. Do not sleep on motorized beds as they create an electrical field.

Use grounding: it repairs radiation damage.
1. Ground by laying on the ground.
2. Sleep on grounding sheets.
3. Utilize grounding mats while working on computers.

Reduce fluorescent lighting where ever possible.
1. Replace fluorescent lights, or use alternate incandescent light sources where possible.
2. Fluorescent lights decrease melatonin, add to the EMF burden, plus can release toxic mercury.

Do not use cell phones, GPS or Bluetooth while driving.
1. The radiations bounce around within the car, increasing their harm.

Do not choose electric, hybrid, or driverless cars.
1. Driving them adds many hours of cumulative EMF radiation exposure.

EMF Safety Check List
Reduce EMF Exposure: Living / Working / Public Areas

Personal Modifications

The following lifestyle changes will go a long way towards decreasing the potential of developing the symptoms and debilitating conditions that have been detailed throughout this book.

Protect your body.
1.   Holding your cell phone makes you an antenna. If possible, place the phone on a desk or surface so you do not have to hold it while using.
2.   Avoid sitting next to others who have wireless devices, as your body is absorbing their radiation.

Eat high antioxidant foods to offset the cellular damage.
Eat organic and non-GMO foods to reduce your toxic intake.
Vitamins C, E.
Green Tea.
Ginkgo biloba.
β-glucan.
CAPE.

Stay hydrated.
1.   Drink plenty of good water (no chlorine or fluoride).
Every cell in the body requires water for proper functioning.

Wear natural fibers, as synthetics attract electricity.
Cotton.
Silk.
Linen.
Wool.
Avoid polyesters.
Wash clothes before wearing as most are coated with chemicals such as formaldehyde to reduce wrinkling during shipping.

Choose safe living and working environments.
1.   If you are moving to a new location, find one that is not near power lines or cell towers, and has living and working spaces as far from smart meters as possible.
2.   Do not choose solar panels until they have been proven to be safe for those living under them. Better to be cautious with something that is difficult to remove after adding to your structure (our EMF sensitive clients have difficulty with the electrical field the DC to AC transformers generate).

Copy and share these lists with family and friends.

.

Chapter 17

A Necessary Course Correction

EHS – Electromagnetic Hypersensitivity Symptoms

In a 2011 review of EMF studies titled: Electromagnetic Hypersensitivity: Fact or Fiction? Dr. Stephen Genuis identified that: "Some scientists and clinicians acknowledge the phenomenon of hypersensitivity to EMR [electromagnetic radiation] resulting from common exposures such as wireless systems and electrical devices in the home or workplace; others suggest electromagnetic hypersensitivity (EHS) is psychosomatic or fictitious."[338]

A review of studies specifically examining electromagnetic hypersensitivity (EHS) concluded that some of the conflicting outcomes and conclusions arise from the fact there is no clear consensus of opinion as to the definition of EHS, and there are too many different scales of measurements. The authors of the review recommended the establishment of a clearly defined definition, along with validated screening tools, which could provide guidance for those in clinical practice who are attempting to help these individuals.[339] Based on these recommendations, it is important to begin to utilize the objective measurements suggested by Drs. Tuengler and von Klitzing of heart rate variability, microcirculation in the capillaries, and electrical potential in the skin as ways to identify those who are electromagnetic hypersensitive (EHS).[340]

EHS – Symptoms Are Validated

The studies clearly show the biochemical reasons why people are experiencing such a wide range of symptoms. Damage to brain cells would lead to loss of memory. Red blood cells changing shape decreases their ability to carry oxygen that results in shortness of breath and headaches. The studies also clearly reveal decreased melatonin, which explains the insomnia others are describing. The proof that EMF open the granules of cells in the skin resulting in the release of histamine and anticoagulant attest to the symptoms of skin itching and bleeding that people report on exposure to cell phones, computers, monitors, and televisions. Laboratory animals displaying activity that indicates they experience ringing in the ears, attest to the fact that this symptom cannot be psychological. Animal studies clearly show that the changes in the biochemistry of increased blood sugar, decreased GABA, increased blood-brain barrier leakage, breakage in their DNA strands, altered calcium balance, and undergoing irreversible infertility are all indicative that EMF radiation affects most of our bodily functions.

There is little information available today that provides suggestions on how to identify and treat the symptoms of EHS. Therefore, this is an unknown field for most health care practitioners and often they do not understand how to recognize or help their electrosensitive patients. This is a difficult and frustrating situation for both the individuals who are suffering, as well as for the health care professionals who are attempting to help them. When a rash broke out all over my body, I saw or consulted with 12 different health care providers who had a wide variety of specialties. Some are very highly regarded in their field, yet none were aware of the concept of how EMF affect the body and that they are capable of creating rashes, or the many other symptoms that people are suffering with today.

In February 2023, as a Clinical Laboratory Scientist, I taught a course on the newly developed lab tests that have been recognized to diagnose EHS. For a test to be valid, there must be measurable changes within the body from EMF that identify the problem. This long needed recognition is the beginning of bringing attention to these debilitating symptoms many people suffer with; and often go from doctor-to-doctor with little recognition of their condition—with no relief.

EHS People Are the Canaries of the Information Age

The difficulty with electromagnetic radiation is that it cannot be seen, just as the bad air in coal mines could not be detected before the miners breathed enough to kill them. To save their lives, they brought in canaries as their early warning sign that the air was toxic. When the canaries stopped singing or dropped dead, it was the signal that they needed to get out of the mine immediately. The people who are showing electrosensitivity symptoms, because they have accumulated more radiation and toxins than their bodies can defend against, are our present day canaries. They are our early warning system for humanity and all other life forms on the planet. We need to heed the signs of toxic stress their bodies are displaying.

Right now it is our modern day canaries who are becoming sick while riding on public transportation or being in buildings serviced by Wi-Fi networks. As the radiation accumulates, a greater and greater percentage will begin to show the symptoms. We need to create EMF free zones on all public transportation as well as in public buildings, the same as the smoke free zones that have been created upon recognition of the danger of cancer from second hand cigarette smoke. EMF free zones are even more imperative, as there is a much wider range of disabilities that are occurring, along with the increased risk of cancer this invisible radiation is capable of creating.

We would like to see the same type of warnings that have been placed on tobacco products sold in many countries around the world be placed on the packaging of all wireless devices also.

Warning	Warning
Wireless devices harm your health and that of others around you.	This area contains radiations known to cause cancer, reproductive harm, Alzheimer's and autism.
Wireless Device Label	**Public Building Poster**

California is requiring all businesses to post signs on their establishments warning people that there are hazardous materials inside. The same type of warning sign needs to be placed on all establishments with Wi-Fi, as well as on public transportation vehicles that allow cell phone use.

The Wireless World's Relentless Expansion

Not only are we being subjected to the radiation from the electronics that are being produced today, we are also subjected to our private information being obtained and shared with corporations who are looking to provide sales ads that are tailored to your specific interests. Please read the June 2015 *Consumer Reports*: Brave New World of Smart Devices – What You Need to Know issue that identifies the problem with the wireless devices having the ability to gather information from your household and share it wherever and with whomever they please. For parents, this includes seeing into your child's bedroom. For the pleasure of having your coffee ready when you want it, and for monitoring your physiology while you are running, having thieves knowing when you are not home.

How could such massive numbers of EMF emitting devices, cell towers, utility smart meters, or public Wi-Fi systems be installed without environmental impact studies being conducted—studies that are demanded for the simple construction of buildings that only impact a small geographical location? The problem with EMF radiation is not only that it cannot be seen, its potential for adverse health conditions takes years to become apparent. When all of the health effects do start manifesting in more and more of the population, it may be that some of the damage will be irreversible.

In the abstract from a 2011 article, researchers from the University of Eastern Finland summarized where we are today and what needs to be done:

> "Man-made electromagnetic irradiation and fields cover now the globe due to the recent extensive propagation of mobile telephony. The increased load affects animals and also plants. Especially birds have been studied. Humans are also sensitive. They are good bioindicators as epidemiological methods are available. Humans can also report symptoms which cannot be directly measured with presently available technologies. The non-ionizing irradiation can as the ionizing one break the DNA, damage proteins, even increase the blood-brain barrier permeability, disturb the night rest, cause fatigue and hormonal disturbances. An increase of the tumors of human head has been described in correla-

tion with the long-term mobile phone use and on that side more exposed. The regulations covering mobile telephony are already about two decades old and need re-evaluation. The multitude of irradiation and the interaction of the different wavelength exposures, i.e., frequency sensitivity is poorly known at present. We should not forget the comparative studies of different species especially those which rely on their lives on electromagnetic orientation physiology. Some countries have issued warnings on the exposures of children. The producers of mobile technology have recently warned the users not to keep those devices in active stage in skin contact."[341]

This book's summary of the physiological impact and resultant health effects is by no means complete. It is truly impossible to comprehend the wide-ranging and far-reaching total health impact that will inevitably arise. With EMF impacting every cell membrane, every organ system has the potential to be altered to some degree. Identifying all the changes in cells, tissues, organs and bodily functions will take years and massive amounts of research. It may never be possible to differentiate the changes, much less understand or comprehend the magnitude of malfunction at the level of every cell that is arising from our biochemistry being altered by our now immersion into continuous EMF radiation.

Already our entire society and health care systems have been altered due to the impact of millions of families struggling with the overwhelming burden of autism and Alzheimer's. The strain on the families alone has changed the very fabric of the family unit. The cost to society of millions unable to be functioning productive members of society and who are incapable of contributing to its success is at a cost in the trillions.

It is estimated that the cost of providing for and taking care of a person with autism in the U.S. is approximately $3.2 million over his or her lifetime. In 2006, the U.S. total estimated cost per year of autism care was $35 billion, and Alzheimer's care was $91 billion.[342] This is a burden that will keep increasing with the increasing incidence of these conditions. As more millions of effected people are added each year, there will eventually be more people who need assistance in daily living than there will be people available to take care of them. No country can survive the financial burden of the medical costs, and cost of lost productivity of both the ever increasing autistic and Alzheimer's populations, as well as their caregivers.

I trust that the research provided in this book leaves you with no doubt there is a certain percentage of the population who are sensitive to EMF today. Everyone is experiencing cumulative effects and the percentage who suffer symptoms will keep rising every year, along with rising medical costs as people seek help to alleviate their symptoms in their attempt to continue being able to function within their families and workplaces.

We all must embrace the admonition of seven researchers from Lund University, in Sweden who in a 2007 presentation to the International Committee on Electromagnetic Safety stated:

"Our generation has introduced the microwaves on Earth. It is our imperative obligation to further investigate and prevent the possible detrimental effects of microwaves upon biology."[343]

> Leif G. Salford, M.D., Ph.D.
> Arne E. Brun, M.D., Ph.D.
> Jacob L. Eberhardt, Ph.D., DMSc
> Gustav Grafstrom, Ph.D.
> Lars O.G. Malmgren, Ph.D.
> Henrietta Nittby, M.D., Ph.D.
> Bertil R. R. Persson, Ph.D., DMSc

Researchers – Take Action

We invite all researchers to read this book in its entirety. Seeing the incontrovertible evidence of the potential for EMF radiation to harm every cell in our body, including destroying the ability to carry on the human race, we trust you will become advocates of reversing the wireless technology revolution and dedicate your research to creating a safe environment where humans are not debilitated and can continue to reproduce.

It is important to remember that because of the lengthy process of developing and conducting a study, as well as getting its results reviewed by a peer review committee and published, most of the literature is outdated, because it was conducted on lower level technologies than the ones currently in use due to the fast changes in technology that keep occurring. Less powerful technologies have proven that harm occurs at much less time than the average user today spends on their wireless devices. Yet, today we hold more powerful devices to our heads and use them for longer than any studies have investigated.

One advertiser (2015) boosts that the average home in the United States has four wireless devices accumulating data (computers / laptops / tablets / smartphones, etc.). We are living in an EMF filled environment that far exceeds the study examples outlined throughout this book.

Congressional hearings have already taken place to study the implementation of even more powerful 5th generation (5G) technologies. We have no idea what those new technologies will bring. Yet, where is the plan for testing the environmental impact on animals or humans before government approval?

The point is that as up-to-date and current as the published findings found within the pages of this book, its information does not reflect the level of power your current smartphone is emitting. As a global community, we will not truly know the impact for the 5 to 10 years it takes the medical and scientific community to determine and publish the actual results. Keep this in mind as you review this material that was conducted on less powerful devices than the world is exposed to today.

Consumers – Take Action

The Consequences of Long-term Cell Phone Use
Is being in constant contact no matter where you are worth:
Brain cancers
Autistic children
Alzheimer's
Body-wide itching
Autoimmune diseases, like MS
Hearing loss
Strokes
Eyesight damage
Food allergies
Inability for many to be in public places?

Governments Not Recognizing EMF Radiation Harm

The U.S. Centers for Disease Control has a website for Frequently Asked Questions about Cell Phones and Your Health. The following questions and answers were posted June 9, 2014:

Q: *Can using a cell phone cause cancer?*
A: There is no scientific evidence that provides a definite answer to that question. Some organizations recommend caution in cell phone use. More research is needed before we know if using cell phones causes health effects.

Q: *Do cell phones give off (emit) radiation?*
A: Yes – cell phones and cordless phones use radiofrequency radiation (RF) to send signals. RF is different from other types of radiation (like x-rays) that we know can be harmful. We don't know for sure if RF radiation from cell phones can cause health problems years later. The International Agency for Research on Cancer (IARC) has classified RF radiation as a "possible human carcinogen." (A carcinogen is an agent that causes cancer.)

Q: *Should people stop using cell phones?*
A: At this time we do not have the science to link health problems to cell phone use. Scientific studies are underway to determine whether cell phone use may cause health effects. It is also important to consider the benefits of cell phones. Their use can be valuable in an urgent or emergency situation – and even save lives.[344]

It is very apparent that the governments that are supposed to enforce guidelines to protect our health and safety do not understand the health threat EMF places on us as well as the lives of all other species. Many governmental radiation safety maximum power limits are above the levels identified as causing harm at the cellular level. Please urge everyone you know to get this book in front of politicians in every country, Senators, Assemblymen, law makers, officers of Public Utility Commissions, City Council members, and managers of all utility companies. Due to a lack of awareness of EMF radiations' true impact, laws and protective measures have been implemented that support the proliferation of wireless services.

Many of the laws, regulations, and safety standards levels need to be reconsidered now that there is substantial evidence of the harm EMF radiation causes society.

It is crucial we take action without delay to protect ourselves, society, and our next generations by reducing our exposure to EMF radiation.

Elizabeth Plourde, C.L.S., NCMP, Ph.D.
Marcus Plourde, Ph.D.
21st Century Health Consulting LLC
Elizabeth@BestEMFProducts.com
Marcus@BestEMFProducts.com

Visit Our Web Sites for Solutions
www.BestEMFProducts.com
www.EMFFreedom.com

Epilogue

5G and Small Cell *Towers* Deployed!

With the demand of bandwidth stretching the Internet providers (IP) capacity to deliver data, it has become necessary to move to 5G (5th generation) service levels. This next higher level makes more bandwidth available to carry the large amounts of data required to connect more people and devices to the Internet. Conservative estimates claim there are 17 billion devices connected to the Internet (early 2023).[345] Service providers are saying the change to 5G allows them to connect up to 100 times more units; create faster download rates with less slowdowns; and significantly increase the capacity to connect all devices to one system. It required moving further up the GHz (gigahertz) frequency scale into the 1-100 GHz, which is the *radar* range.

Interestingly, the 5G bands use millimeter waves (much shorter wave patterns) that are blocked by obstacles like trees, buildings, etc. To compensate for these limitations, the IP service providers have developed ground level small cell systems [notice they are not calling them small cell *towers*] that mount broadband delivery systems on existing telephone and service poles (at 20 feet off the ground). These networks have been installed in an array format throughout our communities. Small boxes must be placed on every 4th or 5th service pole (500 feet apart), possibly on every lamp post, inside every room in homes and businesses to ensure everyone has good reception and faster Internet speeds. This results in more EMF emitting devices and equipment that are located much closer to the users.

If these millimeter waves do not pass through objects that means they are absorbed by whatever is in their way (which could include people, plants, etc.). Should you and your family be so unlucky to have a small cell mounted on the pole in front of your home or business, you cannot contest it being installed even if it is beaming into your or a child's bedroom, nor can you contest the installation for health reasons.

One of the many new technologies unveiled at the 2018 Computer Equipment Show (CES) in Las Vegas are stylish-decorative bookshelf wireless charging systems that can charge all your devices within the room, even while you utilize them. It will charge all the laptops, tablets, fitness trackers, and smartphones in the room without cables. The next development beyond this will be appliances that have no power cords (lamps, televisions). Connections to power outlets will no longer be necessary. Again, there will be units in the corners of each room feeding energy to all the devices in the room that require electricity. This will emit energies that are constantly moving throughout the room. People, children, and pets sitting between the devices being charged and the electrical power unit would have energy traveling through, or absorbed, into their living tissue.

One of the electrical power unit developers has convinced the FCC that the energies from these units will go around the people in the room and not be absorbed, nor impact them. This just does not seem possible, as energies are like water and always follow the path of least resistance. We have not seen whether this type of exposure has been tested to determine whether it would be safe to have in our homes (and bedrooms).

Combine these new technologies with the push to convert vehicles to electric motors, the drive to install *smart home* concepts of needing to integrate and control all your devices (such as Internet connections, thermostats, lights, door bells, security systems, sensors on everything, and so much more). Add a solar panel array above our bedrooms and these "smart" homes are going to be difficult places to live in. Our children and the human race are not going to have much of a chance to develop and thrive. It used to be we would go to our workplace and endure the computers and greater electrical exposures during the day, and we could come home to a safe sanctuary that would allow the body to rest, repair and recover. Today, people are converting their safer sanctuary homes into deadly, toxic environments that compromise their immune systems. With the addition of the higher 5G bandwidth usage, installing small cell *towers* at ground level on our streets, and the addition of all the latest *must-have* technologies, the body's immune system will not be able to keep up with these constant and overwhelming assaults.

6G Pathway Arrays Will Be At Ground Level

They are already working on 6G which will be deployed around 2030. Its communication array will be at ground level. The current designs have the communication pattern moving from one device to another to complete the path to a viable cell tower relay. In other words, my phone is going to connect to your phone, and your phone will connect to the person next to you, until it makes it way to a master relay connection to move the call or the data along to its destination.

We actually have a version of 6G technologies on our homes now, as that is how the utility smart meters communicate. Their data travels from meter-to-meter until it reaches the master hub collection unit that connects to a cell tower. The master hub transfers all the data for the surrounding meters. Driverless vehicle technologies use the same vehicle-to-vehicle communications to manage their tracking of the environment around them.

The Progression of Cell Support Systems

As They Move Closer to Ground Level = People Level

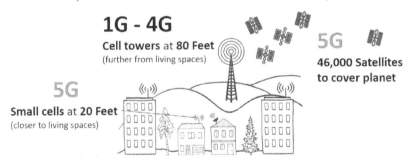

6G arrays will be at Ground Level = People Level

6G **signals** will travel from **device-to-device** at ground level.

The massive race to electrify everything in our world to save the planet is not a good long-term approach, as man-made electricity is severely impacting our health. We recommend reading Arthur Firstenberg's *The Invisible Rainbow: The History of Electricity and Life*. His extensive research confirms that historically, as electricity was deployed throughout the world to modernize our homes and businesses, our health deteriorated. Our body's natural electrical system is just not compatible with man-made electricity.

The secondary research reported by Firstenberg is that with each major change in electrical technologies there has been a pandemic following the deployment of the new device. After the two-way radio was deployed by the military, the 1918 Spanish flu followed. After radar was deployed and after the over-the-horizon missile detection systems were turned on, pandemics followed.[346] Flu like conditions may mostly be EMF symptoms from the overwhelming changes in the earth's electrical energies.

We believe the changes we are going to experience in the next few years may be the tipping point that will impact the health of the human race, and all life on the planet. Our overall health will deteriorate so rapidly that the scientific and medical communities will have to finally acknowledge the damage from the vast number of electromagnetic fields, which were not as prevalent just 30 years ago. By then, it may be too late to repair the DNA damage it is capable of causing. We and many scientists around the world know that the plethora of energies we have surrounded ourselves with are toxic to the body. These massive changes in our exposures to EMF will create significant detrimental changes in our health and that of the planet as a whole.

Resources

EMF Products We Use and Recommend
Survival Solutions For Living In the Digital Age

www.*BestEMFProducts*.com

Smart DOTs
For Cell Phones
and Electronics

Body/Bio DOTs
Wearables
For Your Family

**Wearable
Options**

TAGs / Pendants

Wrist Bands

CLIPs

Adhesive DOTs

For Wireless Devices
**Wi-Fi Routers
Computers
Laptops
Printers
Keyboards
Mouse
Baby monitors
Video Consoles
Smart TVs**
Kitchen Appliances
Washers / Dryers

Security Systems

Vehicle Electronics

Make All Your Environments Safer!

We Offer the Products that Work For Us

As medical researchers and personal users of EMF products, our commitment is to act on your behalf to seek out and offer only the "best EMF products" available.

www.*BestEMFProducts*.com

See the following pages for the details as to
why Smart DOT products are different!

Why Smart/Energy DOT Products Are Different!

Energy Optimizers
Promote Life, Growth, and Better Long-term Health

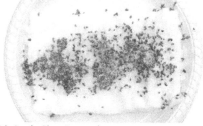

Phi Harmonics, LLC.   9th Grade Class-Denmark Reprinted with permission.

Cress seeds next to Wi-Fi   **Cress seeds died without DOT**
grew and thrived with DOT   (from experiment on page 64)

No matter where people go today, there is so much radiation it is imperative for everyone to protect their bodies utilizing energy optimizers for their personal space, as well as by placing harmonizers on their electronic equipment. There are many EMF devices available today that are being marketed as protection from the radiation. We, along with many others, found that "most do not work." Some actually make people feel worse rather than better, which is what happened to me as I became sicker and sicker wearing various types of pendants and using energy blockers on our devices.

Blockers and shielding devices can make cell phones more harmful as they have to power up (at the phone) to reach the cell tower (to make up for the weaker signal). The cell companies themselves, warn not to use your phone when you only have a 1 bar reception area for this reason. In general, conceptually, the blockers and shielding devices would make the phone function like it is in a low reception area.

The only reason I could finish writing this book, and then update it two years later, is due to using the Energy DOTs that offer harmonic technologies. In the first few days of using them, I could be back in public and in a week could use a cell phone and computer again, which I had not been able to do for 4 months. I had to withdraw from public places because it was too painful to feel the sharp needles I felt in my body from cell phones and smart meters. The Energy DOT products are the only ones that brought me relief and provided the ability to reenter the world as a productive human being. The following are detailed explanations of how they work and why they are more effective.

Smart/Energy DOT Technologies

Energy DOT technologies carry a unique resonant signature designed primarily to counteract negative health effects from exposure to man-made electromagnetic fields. This vibrational information is infused onto a magnetic tape, like those used on credit cards, and is the active principle used to carry the DOT's energy signature. There are several DOTs within the system and each are specifically programmed to work with different energy fields. As such, they are color coded for each energy they work with and are not interchangeable. When used for their intended purpose, they are the best EMF products that we have found to work for us.

Energy DOTs Utilize the Golden Mean Ratio

The classically known Golden Mean Ratio, also known as Fibonacci sequence (nature's code), has been used throughout time to create harmony in art, architecture and music. It has an organizing effect at a vibrational level. In its highest form, it can be expressed as a mathematical ratio that expresses how nature creates everything in perfect harmony.

The vibrational information on the Smart DOT "teaches" the man-made EMF energies how to resonate with natural coherence. It retunes the energy emissions of the device at a subtle level without interfering with the efficiency of device's operation (e.g., cell phone, tablet, computer, etc.). Since it is not blocking or shielding the phone's energies, the phone and Wi-Fi services operate at full signal strength with no reduction in its ability to function.

Future Science

When an Energy DOT is placed on or near EMF emitting equipment, it "harmonizes" the artificially generated electro-magnetic fields. This occurs through the process of entrainment. The Energy DOT's resonant signature interacts with the frequencies of the equipment/person/water/space to bring about a state of natural coherence that is less intrusive and is life enhancing to hu-

---

man physiology. They make each of us healthier, and assisting our immune system to better handle the assault it must endure each day. It is the result of a new futurist form of medicine This new form of medicine, known as information medicine, will take us into the future to produce better health. We are grateful that this type of futuristic science is available today to address the EMF pollutions of the 21st century.

Using Energy DOTs Effectively

Smart DOTs For Electronic Devices

Smart DOTs are designed to reduce the harmful impact of electronic, Wi-Fi, and the new more powerful smartphones and smart electronics. These units can be attached with a sticky adhesive to any device or appliance. Do incorporate these on as many electrical devices that you can to offset their EMF energies.

Personal Wearable Devices

The Body/Bio DOT strengthens your body's energy field. It helped me to once again be around cell phones, computers, and Wi-Fi, which is important considering the sea of EMF that now surrounds us everywhere. These can be obtained in the form of pendants, key chain clips, wrist bands, or small individual DOTs that can be attached to your own jewelry or watch. Just as you eat the right food for your physical body, they provide your energy field with the right energy, and well worth investing in to assist your energy balance throughout the day.

Do not overlook the wearable products, as they are what makes it possible for me to be in public places. They are the first product the inventor produced for her own EMF sensitivities.

The Energy DOT System Works Together: Restoring Balance to Achieve Better Health

Smart DOT products work synergistically to make the body healthier so it can better withstand the EMF assault it must face everyday. They work to increase the flow of oxygen to the body's organs and cells, reduce inflammation, and strengthen the body's biofield. These changes within the body produce better long-term results than any effort to block or shield the EMF energies emitted from electronic and electrical devices.

Why Smart DOT Products Are Different:
<u>They Create Healthy Changes Within the Body</u>

**Red blood cells (RBC) are separated to allow them
to deliver vital-to-life oxygen to the organs and cells:**
the body can do without water and food, but oxygen is needed!

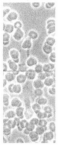   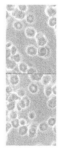

Baseline	1 hour on cell	Energy DOT	**1 hour with DOT**
	No DOT	added	= frees up RBCs

Strengthen the body's natural energetic biofield:
creates fewer holes, less chaos, and less energy loss.

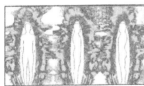 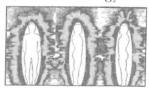

Before   **After 2 days**

Reduces Inflammation

**Energy DOTs
have a cumulative-effect:**
The body becomes
stronger over time with use.

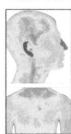 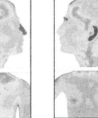

Before   **After 21 days**

Changes within the body are *much better measurements* to
show us how these products can impact our long-term health!

Our Product Testing

As medical researchers, we keep exploring the marketplace to find EMF products for our own use. We are both sensitive and Elizabeth is very sensitive. We test the new device by itself. So far, every one tested has brought Elizabeth back to the place where was at before she started using the Smart DOT products. (Her first symptom is that she begins itching up her mouse hand and arm.)

As we have tested more and more products, we have come to the conclusion that the inventor of the Energy DOTs system got it right the first time. Many of the newcomers to the marketplace are working to clone or copy them, as the Energy DOTs are the **"Gold Standard"** within the industry.

A Final Word

Today, we have EMF energies traveling through the air from every direction at levels and in quantities that we have never experienced. It is totally impossible to block and shield us from the 360 degree assault. The blocking and shielding can make them more harmful, as it can force the rerouted energies to become concentrated into more powerful beams.

Smart DOT products work to change the electromagnetic energies electronics produce to become more human-compatible. They are much better options for the 21st century world we live in, as we make every effort to remain healthy and thrive.

As our research for ourselves is always ongoing, visit our websites to view our current product recommendations:

www.**BestEMFProducts**.com

www.**SmartDOTs**.us

www.**EMFFreedom**.com

Websites are not always user-friendly or they may not answer all your questions. Please feel free to contract us. We are here to help:

Marcus@BestEMFProducts.com

Elizabeth@BestEMFProducts.com

Recommended Reading and Films

Reading

We highly recommend reading:

Firstenberg A. *The Invisible Rainbow: The History of Electricity and Life*. Chelsea Green Publishing; 2020.

This extensive research **confirms** that historically, as electricity was deployed to modernize our homes and businesses, our health deteriorated.

Becker R. *Cross Currents*. Tarcher (1990).

Becker R, Selden G. *The Body Electric: Electromagnetism and the Foundation of Life*. William Morrow Paperbacks; 1st edition 1998.

Crofton, K. *A Wellness Guide for The Digital Age: With Safer-tech Solutions for All Things Wired & Wireless*. Global Wellbeing Books; 2013.

Crofton, K. *Wireless Radiation Rescue - 2012: How to Use Cell Phones More Safely and Other Safer-Tech Solutions*. Global Wellbeing Books; 3rd edition 2011.

Davis, D. *Disconnect: The Truth About Cell Phone Radiation* Environmental Health Trust; 2013.

Gittleman AL. *Zapped: Why Your Cell Phone Shouldn't Be Your Alarm Clock and 1,268 Ways to Outsmart the Hazards of Electronic Pollution*. HarperOne; Reprint edition 2011.

Levitt BB. *Electromagnetic Fields: A Consumer's Guide to the Issues and How to Protect Ourselves*. Backinprint.com 2007.

Ober C, Sinatra ST, Zucker M. *Earthing: The Most Important Health Discovery Ever?* Basic Health Publications; 1st edition 2010.

Plourde, E. *Sunscreens – Biohazard: Treat As Hazardous Waste.* New Voice Publications; Irvine, CA 2011.

Plourde, E, Plourde M. *Sunscreens – Biohazard 2: Proof of Toxicity Keeps Piling Up.* New Voice Publications; Irvine, CA 2018.

Rees C, Havas M. *Public Health SOS: the Shadow Side of the Wireless Revolution.* CreateSpace Independent Publishing Platform; 1st edition 2009.

Singer D. *An Electronic Silent Spring: Facing the Dangers and Creating Safe Limits.* Portal Books. 2014

Talbott D, Thornhill W. *The Electric Universe.* Mikamar Publishing; 2007.

Films

"Connect." Cinedigm Entertainment. Released 2018.

"Generation Zapped." Studio: Zapped Productions, LLC. Released 2017.

"Take Back Your Power: Investigating the Smart Grid." Studio: Passion River. Released 2013.

Resources

The BioInitiative Report 2012
A Rationale for Biologically-based Public Exposure Standards for Electromagnetic Fields (ELF and RF).

This 1,479 page report, by 29 distinguished and highly recognized EMF experts from around the world, presents more than enough research evidence to help us recognize that it is essential for us to immediately start taking the steps that will reverse the EMF inundation upon the planet. The full report is available at: www.bioinitiative.org

Authors: Cindy Sage, MA
David O. Carpenter, MD
Jitendra Behari, PhD
Carlo V. Bellieni, MD
Igor Belyaev, Dr. Sc.
Carl F. Blackman, PhD
Martin Blank, PhD
Michael Carlberg, MSc
Zoreh Davanipour, DVM, PhD
David Gee, Senior Advisor
Adamantia F. Fragopoulou, PhD
Yury Grigoriev, MD
Kjell Hansson Mild, PhD
Lennart Hardell, MD, PhD
Martha Herbert, PhD, MD
Paul Héroux, PhD
Michael Kundi, PhD
Henry Lai, PhD
Abraham R Liboff, PhD
Ying Li, PhD
Lukas H. Margaritis, PhD
Henrietta Nittby, MD, PhD
Bertil R. Persson, PhD, MD h.c.
Gerd Oberfeld, MD
Iole Pinto, PhD
Paulraj Rajamani, PhD
Leif Salford, MD, PhD
Eugene Sobel, PhD
Amy Thomsen, MPH, MSPAS, PA-C

Resources

NewsFlash Newsletter
Health Information You Can Trust

Technology is developing so rapidly we realize that the best way to keep you informed of the latest types of protection from EMF is through our newsletter, *NewsFlash*. We started it to inform the public of health information they deserve to know, which now necessarily encompasses EMF radiation information.

This succinct health newsletter is designed to fit into your busy schedule, while providing you with information everyone needs to sort through the avalanche of medical news and products hitting the shelves. *NewsFlash* is available for you and your family at:

www.BestEMFProducts.com/books.html

NewsFlash
Health Information You Can Trust

Sunscreens' Multiple Links to Autism

Beware!
Pregnant Women – Infants – Children
Especially Females

Contained in this issue:
- Sunscreens Do Not Perform As Marketed
- UCLA & MIT Researchers Substantiate Sunscreens' Link to ADHD & Autism
- Toxic Chemical Disrupts Normal Nerve Cell Development in Brain
- Vitamin D Identified As Essential for Proper Nerve Cell Development
- Vitamin D Needed for Essential Brain Nerve Cell "Pruning"

Resources

Sunscreens Biohazard: Treat as Hazardous Waste

Sunscreens Biohazard 2: Proof of Toxicity Keeps Piling Up

Toxins that Are Impacting Our Health

This book details why sunscreen chemicals do not protect from skin cancers and photoaging and why antioxidants should be utilized in their place. It includes a comprehensive list of the antioxidant foods that are proven to protect from solar radiation. The protection they display in shielding against solar radiation demonstrates they would be capable of providing the same protection from EMF radiation as well.

Sunscreens were never proven to prevent melanoma or basal cell carcinoma, yet all of the chemicals approved by the FDA are toxic. This includes even the ones that manufacturers label as "kid safe", one of which is titanium dioxide is detrimental to fetal brain development, since it is not only incorporated into sunscreens, all women and young girls need to avoid makeup with an SPF rating as it is usually titanium dioxide. It is also in white foods, gum, candies and tooth paste, etc.

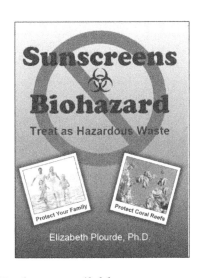

Both are available at:

Includes updated research!

www.SunscreensBiohazard.com

Picture Credits

Cover: Background: 123rf.com/Givaga
Cell tower: 123rf.com/Chichimaru
Cell phone: Wikimedia Commons/Irfan Nasir
Wi-Fi router: Wikimedia Commons/Rewt
Smart meter: 123rf.com/pixelrobot
Baby: 123rf.com/Anitap
Sunscreen bottle: 123rf.com/Zoomzoom

Page #s
27 Puzzle istockphoto.com/RelaxFoto.de
32 & 33
MRI/radio towers/radar: taken from: Consales C, Merla C,
Marino C, Benassi B. Electromagnetic fields, oxidative stress, and
neurodegeneration. *Int J Cell Biol.* 2012;2012:683897. Epub 2012 Sep 9.
Reprinted with permission.
Bluetooth: Wikimedia Commons/Ed g2s
Cell phone: Wikimedia Commons/Irfan Nasir
Cordless phone: Wikimedia Commons/Pbroks13
Laptop: Wikimedia Commons/Kelvin sze
Microwave oven: Wikimedia Commons/DorisRHanlin
Power lines: Wikimedia Commons/Yummifruitbat
Smart meter: 123rf.com/pixelrobot
Television: Wikimedia Commons/Wags05
Wi-Fi logo: Wikimedia Commons/Wi-Fi Alliance
Wi-Fi router: Wikimedia Commons/Rewt
38 Smart meter - upper: 123rf.com/pixelrobot
Smart meter - lower: 123rf.com/funniefarm5
51 Cell: Wikimedia Commons/Dhatfield
56 DNA strand: Wikimedia Commons/Richard Wheeler (Zephyris)
59 & 62 Tight junction: Wikimedia Commons/Mariana Ruiz LadyofHats
63 Intestines: Wikimedia Commons/William Crochot/www.cancer.
gov/cancertopics/wyntk/colon-and-rectum
70 Red blood cells: NIH public domain
81 Purkinje cell: The Florida Center for Instructional Technology Clip art
#53184
82 Cerebellum: 123rf.com/alila
92 Pyramidal cells: Wikimedia Commons/Nrets
95 Mast cells: Wikimedia Commons/Kauczuk
98 Bullseye rash: Wikimedia Commons/Optigan13

References

Please spend a few moments to just read the titles, as they will provide insight into how electromagnetic fields are impacting our health.

1 Frey AH. **Data analysis reveals significant microwave-induced eye damage in humans. J Microw Power** *Electromagn Energy.* 1985; 20(1):53-55.

2 Huss, J. Committee on the Environment, Agriculture and Local and Regional Affairs Parliamentary Assembly, Council of Europe. May 6, 2011. Doc. 12608.

3 Nittby H, Grafström G, Tian DP. **Cognitive impairment in rats after long-term exposure to GSM-900 mobile phone radiation.** *Bioelectromagnetics.* 2008;29(3):219-232.

4 How Many Are There website. **How many mobile phone users are there.** Retrieved March 20, 2013 from: www.howmanyarethere.org/how-many-mobile-phone-users-in-us/

   Wikipedia website. **List of countries by number of mobile phones in use.** Retrieved June 6, 2015 from: http://en.wikipedia.org/wiki/List_of_countries_by_number_of_mobile_phones_in_use

5 Urbinello D, Röösli M. **Impact of one's own mobile phone in stand-by mode on personal radiofrequency electromagnetic field exposure.** *J Expo Sci Environ Epidemiol.* 2012. doi: 10.1038/jes.2012.97. [Epub ahead of print]. Abstract only.

6 U.S. FCC website. **Specific Absorption Rate (SAR) for Cellular Telephones.** Retrieved July 4, 2015 from: www.fcc.gov/search/#q=specific absorption rate

7 Panagopoulos DJ, Johansson O, Carlo GL. **Evaluation of specific absorption rate as a dosimetric quantity for electromagnetic fields bioeffects.** *PLoS One.* 2013;8(6):e62663. doi: 10.1371/journal.pone.0062663. Print 2013.

8 Pall ML. **Microwave frequency electromagnetic fields (EMFs) produce widespread neuropsychiatric effects including depression.** *J Chem Neuroanat.* 2015 Aug 21. pii: S0891-0618(15)00059-9. doi: 10.1016/j.jchemneu.2015.08.001. [Epub ahead of print].

   Pall ML. **Scientific evidence contradicts findings and assumptions of Canadian Safety Panel 6: microwaves act through voltage-gated calcium channel activation to induce biological impacts at non-thermal levels, supporting a paradigm shift for microwave/lower frequency electromagnetic field action.** *Rev Environ Health.* 2015;30(2):99-116. doi: 10.1515/reveh-2015-0001.

9 Forbes website. Probasco J. **Google might be planning free nationwide Wi-Fi since the FCC isn't.** Retrieved April 8, 2013 from: www.forbes.com/sites/benzingainsights/2013/04/08/google-might-be-planning-free-nationwide-wi-fi-since-the-fcc-isnt/

10 San Diego Gas & Electric website. **Radio frequency concerns: smart meter technology and products.** Retrieved March 20, 2013 from: www.sdge.com/residential/about-smart-meters/radio-frequency-concerns

   Pacific Gas & Electric website. **Radio frequency FAQ: what is "radio frequency"?** Retrieved March 20, 2013 from: www.pge.com/myhome/edusafety/systemworks/rf/faq/

   Southern California Gas website. Learn more about advanced meter technology features and benefits. Retrieved November 25, 2015 from: www.socalgas.com/save-money-and-energy/advanced-meter/about-the-program

REFERENCES

11 Maine Coalition to Stop Smart Meters website. **Smart Meter Health Effects Survey and Report.** Retrieved August 1, 2015 from: www.mainecoalitiontostopsmartmeters.org/wp-content/uploads/2013/01/Exhibit-10-Smart-Meter-Health-Effects-Report-Survey2.pdf

12 Beason RC, Semm P. **Responses of neurons to an amplitude modulated microwave stimulus.** *Neurosci Lett.* 2002;333(3):175-178.

13 Shahbazi-Gahrouei D, Karbalae M, Moradi HA, Baradaran-Ghahfarokhi M. **Health effects of living near mobile phone base transceiver station (BTS) antennae: a report from Isfahan, Iran.** *Electromagn Biol Med.* 2014;33(3):206-10. doi: 10.3109/15368378.2013.801352. [Epub 2013 Jun 19].

14 U.S. NASA website. **RF & Microwave Radiation Hazard Awareness.** Retrieved June 1, 2015 from: www.sites.wff.nasa.gov/code803/docs/RF%20 Awareness%20Training%205-2013.pdf

15 Jauchem JR, Merritt JH. **The epidemiology of exposure to electromagnetic fields: an overview of the recent literature.** *J Clin Epidemiol.* 1991;44(9):895-906.

16 Simkó M, Kriehuber R, Lange S. **Micronucleus formation in human amnion cells after exposure to 50 Hz MF applied horizontally and vertically.** *Mutat Res.* 1998;418(2-3):101-111.

17 Naira B, Yerazik M, Anna N, Sinerik A. **The impact of background radiation, illumination and temperature on EMF-induced changes of aqua medium properties.** *Electromagn Biol Med.* 2013;32(3):390-400. doi: 10.3109/15368378.2012.735206. [Epub 2013 Jan 16].

18 Simkó M. **Induction of cell activation processes by low frequency electromagnetic fields.** *Scientific World Journal.* 2004;4(S2):4–22. ISSN 1537-744X; DOI 10.1100/tsw.2004.174.

19 U.S. EPA website. **A framework for assessing health risk of environmental exposures to children (final).** U.S. Environmental Protection Agency, Washington, DC, EPA/600/R-05/093F, 2006. Retrieved March 15, 2013 from: http://cfpub.epa.gov/ncea/risk/recordisplay.cfm?deid=158363
Makris SL, Thompson CM, Euling SY, Selevan SG, Sonawane B. **A lifestage-specific approach to hazard and dose-response characterization for children's health risk assessment.** *Birth Defects Res B Dev Reprod Toxicol.* 2008;83(6):530-546. Abstract only.

20 Genuis SJ. **Fielding a current idea: exploring the public health impact of electromagnetic radiation.** *Public Health.* 2008;122(2):113-124. [Epub 2007 Jun 18].

21 Fragopoulou A, Grigoriev Y, Johansson O, et al. **Scientific panel on electromagnetic field health risks: consensus points, recommendations, and rationales.** *Rev Environ Health.* 2010;25(4):307-317. Abstract only.

22 Dämvik M, Johansson O. **Health risk assessment of electromagnetic fields: a conflict between the precautionary principle and environmental medicine methodology.** *Rev Environ Health.* 2010;25(4):325-333. Abstract only.

23 Röösli M, Hug K. **Wireless communication fields and non-specific symptoms of ill health: a literature review.** *Wien Med Wochenschr.* 2011;161(9-10):240-250.

24 Cucurachi S, Tamis WL, Vijver MG, Peijnenburg WJ, Bolte JF, de Snoo GR. **A review of the ecological effects of radiofrequency electro-magnetic fields (RF-EMF).** *Environ Int.* 2013;51:116-140. doi: 10.1016/j.envint.2012.10.009. [Epub 2012 Dec 20].

25 Alzheimer's Association International website. **World Alzheimers Report 2015 - Summary Sheet.** Retrieved February 12, 2106 from: www.alz.co.uk/research/world-report-2015
Alzheimer's Association website. **World Alzheimer Report 2009 Executive Summary.** Retrieved March 20, 2013 from: www.alz.org/national/documents/report_summary_2009worldalzheimerreport.pdf

26 Alzheimer's Association International website. **World Alzheimers Report 2015 - Summary Sheet.** Retrieved February 12, 2106 from: www.alz.co.uk/research/world-report-2015

Hebert LE, Weuve J, Scherr PA, Evans DA. **Alzheimer disease in the United States (2010–2050) estimated using the 2010 Census.** *Neurology.* 2013;80(19):1778–1783.

Alzheimer's Association website. **2015 Alzheimer's Disease Facts and Figures.** Retrieved February 12, 2016 from: www.alz.org/facts/overview.asp

27 Natural Solutions Magazine website. **The autoimmune disease riddle.** Retrieved from January 12, 2010 from: www.naturalsolutionsmag.com/index.cfm/fuseaction/center.article/articleID/12801/subTopicID/27/TheAutoimmuneDiseaseRiddle

28 Natural Solutions Magazine website. **The autoimmune disease riddle.** Retrieved from January 12, 2010 from: www.naturalsolutionsmag.com/index.cfm/fuseaction/center.article/articleID/12801/subTopicID/27/TheAutoimmuneDiseaseRiddle

29 Phys.org website. **Asthma rates and where you live: a new study shows how neighborhood characteristics play a significant role in childhood asthma (2009).** Children's Memorial Hospital. Retrieved March 20, 2013 from: www.physorg.com/news163425208.html

Pallarito K. **Dust exposure after 9/11 linked to high asthma rates (2009).** Retrieved March 20, 2013 from: www.cnn.com/2009/HEALTH/08/05/dust.exposure.asthma/index.html.

30 Wild S, Roglic G, Green A, Sicree R, King H. **Global prevalence of diabetes: estimates for the year 2000 and projections for 2030.** *Diabetes Care.* 2004;27(5):1047-1053.

31 Health Intelligence website. **Prevalence of Diabetes in the World, 2013.** Retrieved July 12, 2015 from: http://healthintelligence.drupalgardens.com/content/prevalence-diabetes-world-2013

32 Wild S, Roglic G, Green A, Sicree R, King H. **Global prevalence of diabetes: estimates for the year 2000 and projections for 2030.** *Diabetes Care.* 2004;27(5):1047-1053.

33 American Diabetes Assoc. website. **Statistics about diabetes.** Retrieved July 12, 2015 from: www.diabetes.org/diabetes-basics/statistics/

34 American Heart Association website. **Statistical Fact Sheet 2013 Update.** Retrieved March 11, 2013 from: www.heart.org/idc/groups/heart-public/@wcm/@sop/@smd/documents/downloadable/ucm_319588.pdf

35 BBC News website. **Strokes rising among people of working age, warns charity.** Retrieved June 1, 2015 from: www.bbc.com/news/health-32690040

36 Kissela BM, Khoury JC, Alwell K, et al. **Age at stroke: temporal trends in stroke incidence in a large, biracial population.** *Neurology.* 2012;79(17):1781-1787. doi: 10.1212/WNL.0b013e318270401d. [Epub 2012 Oct 10].

37 Treffert DA. **Autistic disorder 52 years later: some common sense conclusions.** Retrieved March 20, 2013 from: www.wisconsinmedicalsociety.org/professional/savant-syndrome/resources/articles/4907-2/.

Wallis C. **New studies see a higher rate of autism: is the jump real?** *Time* Magazine website. Retrieved March 20, 2013 from: www.time.com/time/health/article/0,8599,1927824,00.html.

Baio J. **Prevalence of Autism Spectrum Disorder Among Children Aged 8 Years — Autism and Developmental Disabilities Monitoring Network, 11 Sites, United States,** *2010 Surveillance Summaries.* March 28, 2014 / 63(SS02);1-21.

Maenner MJ, Shaw KA, Bakian AV, et al. **Prevalence and Characteristics of Autism Spectrum Disorder Among Children Aged 8 Years—Autism and Developmental Disabilities Monitoring Network, 11 Sites, United States, 2018.** MMWR Surveill Summ 2021;70(No. SS-11):1–16.

Autism Speaks Website. **Autism Statistics and Facts.** Retrieved Feb. 10, 2023 from: www.autismspeaks.org/autism-statistics-asd.

38   Seneff S. **Cindy & Erica's Obsession to Solve Today's Health Care Crisis: Autism, Alzheimer's Disease, Cardiovascular Disease, ALS and More.** New Voice Publications. Irvine CA. 2017.
39   Moreno C, Laje G, Blanco C, Jiang H, Schmidt AB, Olfson M. **National trends in the outpatient diagnosis and treatment of bipolar disorder in youth.** *Arch Gen Psychiatry.* 2007;64(9):1032-1039.
40   Morabito C, Rovetta F, Bizzarri M, Mazzoleni G, Fano G, Mariggio MA. **Modulation of redox status and calcium handling by extremely low frequency electromagnetic fields in C2C12 muscle cells: a real-time, single-cell approach.** *Free Radic Biol Med.* 2010;48(4):579-589. [Epub 2009 Dec 11]. Abstract only.
     Pall ML. **Microwave frequency electromagnetic fields (EMFs) produce widespread neuropsychiatric effects including depression.** *J Chem Neuroanat.* 2015 Aug 21. pii: S0891-0618(15)00059-9. doi: 10.1016/j. jchemneu.2015.08.001. [Epub ahead of print].
41   Wang X, Bukoreshtliev NV, Gerdes HH. **Developing neurons form transient nanotubes facilitating electrical coupling and calcium signaling with distant astrocytes.** *PLoS One.* 2012;7(10):e47429. doi: 10.1371/journal. pone.0047429. [Epub 2012 Oct 11].
     Perea G, Araque A. **Glial calcium signaling and neuron-glia communication.** *Cell Calcium.* 2005;38(3-4):375-382.
42   Maskey D, Kim HJ, Kim HG, Kim MJ. **Calcium-binding proteins and GFAP immunoreactivity alterations in murine hippocampus after 1 month of exposure to 835 MHz radiofrequency from SAR values of 1.6 and 4.0 W/ kg.** *Neurosci Lett.* 2012;506(2):292-296. doi: 10.1016/j.neulet. 2011.11.025. [Epub 2011 Nov 25].
43   Martínez-Sámano J, Torres-Durán PV, Juárez-Oropeza MA, Verdugo-Diaz L. **Effect of acute extremely low frequency electromagnetic field exposure on the antioxidant status and lipid levels in rat brain.** *Arch Med Res.* 2012;43(3):183-189. [Epub 2012 May 3].
44   Simkó M, Mattsson MO. **Extremely low frequency electromagnetic fields as effectors of cellular responses in vitro: possible immune cell activation.** *J Cell Biochem.* 2004;93(1):83-92. Abstract only.
45   Simkó M. **Induction of cell activation processes by low frequency electromagnetic fields.** *Scientific World Journal.* 2004;4(S2): 4–22. ISSN 1537-744X; DOI 10.1100/tsw.2004.174.
46   Kesari KK, Behari J, Kumar S. **Mutagenic response of 2.45 GHz radiation exposure on rat brain.** *Int J Radiat Biol.* 2010;86(4):334-343. doi: 10.3109/09553000903564059.
     Behari J, Paulraj R. **Biomarkers of induced electromagnetic field and cancer.** *Indian J Exp Biol.* 2007;45(1):77-85.
47   Bilgici B, Akar A, Avci B, Tuncel OK. **Effect of 900 MHz radiofrequency radiation on oxidative stress in rat brain and serum.** *Electromagn Biol Med.* 2013 Jan 9. [Epub ahead of print].
48   Avci B, Akar A, Bilgici B, Tunçel ÖK. **Oxidative stress induced by 1.8 GHz radio frequency electromagnetic radiation and effects of garlic extract in rats.** *Int J Radiat Biol.* 2012;88(11):799-805. doi: 10.3109/09553002.2012.711504. [Epub 2012 Aug 8].
49   Kesari KK, Kumar S, Behari J. **900-MHz microwave radiation promotes oxidation in rat brain.** *Electromagn Biol Med.* 2011;30(4):219-234. doi: 10.3109/15368378.2011.587930.
50   Morabito C, Rovetta F, Bizzarri M, Mazzoleni G, Fano G, Mariggio MA. **Modulation of redox status and calcium handling by extremely low frequency electromagnetic fields in C2C12 muscle cells: a real-time, single-cell approach.** *Free Radic Biol Med.* 2010;48(4):579-589. [Epub 2009 Dec 11]. Abstract only.

51 Valko M, Leibfritz D, Moncol J, Cronin MT, Mazur M, Telser J. **Free radicals and antioxidants in normal physiological functions and human disease.** *Int J Biochem Cell Biol.* 2007;39(1):44-84. [Epub 2006 Aug 4].
52 Blank M, Goodman R. **Electromagnetic fields stress living cells.** *Pathophysiology.* 2009;16(2-3):71-78. doi: 10.1016/j.pathophys.2009.01.006. [Epub 2009 Mar 5].
53 Blank M, Goodman R. **DNA is a fractal antenna in electromagnetic fields.** *Int J Radiat Biol.* 2011;87(4):409-415. doi: 10.3109/09553002.2011.538130. [Epub 2011 Feb 28].
54 Franzellitti S, Valbonesi P, Ciancaglini N, et al. **Transient DNA damage induced by high-frequency electromagnetic fields (GSM 1.8 GHz) in the human trophoblast HTR-8/SVneo cell line evaluated with the alkaline comet assay.** *Mutat Res.* 2010;683(1-2):35-42.
55 Hekmat A, Saboury AA, Moosavi-Movahedi AA. **The toxic effects of mobile phone radiofrequency (940MHz) on the structure of calf thymus DNA.** *Ecotoxicol Environ Saf.* 2013;88:35-41. doi: 10.1016/j.ecoenv.2012.10.016. [Epub 2012 Nov 17].
56 Gye MC, Park CJ. **Effect of electromagnetic field exposure on the reproductive system.** *Clin Exp Reprod Med.* 2012;39(1):1-9. doi: 10.5653/cerm.2012.39.1.1. [Epub 2012 Mar 31].
Note: Addditional footnotes related to chart built by Gye and Park:
a Lindström E, Mild KH, Lundgren E. **Analysis of the T cell activation signaling pathway during ELF magnetic field exposure, p56lck and [Ca2+]i-measurements.** *Bioelectrochem Bioenerget.* 1998;46:129–137.
b Liburdy RP. **Calcium signaling in lymphocytes and ELF fields. Evidence for an electric field metric and a site of interaction involving the calcium ion channel.** *FEBS Lett.* 1992;301:53–59.
c Leszczynski D, Joenväärä S, Reivinen J, Kuokka R. **Non-thermal activation of the hsp27/p38MAPK stress pathway by mobile phone radiation in human endothelial cells: molecular mechanism for cancer- and blood-brain barrier-related effects.** *Differentiation.* 2002;70:120–129.
d Goodman R, Blank M. **Insights into electromagnetic interaction mechanisms.** *J Cell Physiol.* 2002;192:16–22.
e Koh EK, Ryu BK, Jeong DY, Bang IS, Nam MH, Chae KS. **A 60-Hz sinusoidal magnetic field induces apoptosis of prostate cancer cells through reactive oxygen species.** *Int J Radiat Biol.* 2008;84:945–955.
f Zimmerman JW, Pennison MJ, Brezovich I, et al. **Cancer cell proliferation is inhibited by specific modulation frequencies.** *Br J Cancer.* 2012;106:307–313.
g Sarkar S, Ali S, Behari J. **Effect of low power microwave on the mouse genome: a direct DNA analysis.** *Mutat Res.* 1994;320:141–147.
h Diem E, Schwarz C, Adlkofer F, Jahn O, Rüdiger H. **Non-thermal DNA breakage by mobile-phone radiation (1800 MHz) in human fibroblasts and in transformed GFSH-R17 rat granulosa cells in vitro.** *Mutat Res.* 2005;583:178–183.
i Aitken RJ, Bennetts LE, Sawyer D, Wiklendt AM, King BV. **Impact of radio frequency electromagnetic radiation on DNA integrity in the male germline.** *Int J Androl.* 2005;28:171–179.
j Nikolova T, Czyz J, Rolletschek A, Blyszczuk P, Fuchs J, Jovtchev G, et al. **Electromagnetic fields affect transcript levels of apoptosis-related genes in embryonic stem cell-derived neural progenitor cells.** *FASEB J.* 2005;19:1686–1688.
k Zeni O, Di Pietro R, d'Ambrosio G, et al. **Formation of reactive oxygen species in L929 cells after exposure to 900 MHz RF radiation with and without co-exposure to 3-chloro-4-(dichloromethyl)-5-hydroxy-2(5H)-furanone.** *Radiat Res.* 2007;167:306–311.
Continued on next page

l   Zeni O, Di Pietro R, d'Ambrosio G, Massa R, Capri M, Naarala J, et al. **Formation of reactive oxygen species in L929 cells after exposure to 900 MHz RF radiation with and without co-exposure to 3-chloro-4-(dichloromethyl)-5-hydroxy-2(5H)-furanone.** *Radiat Res.* 2007;167:306–311.

m   Luukkonen J, Hakulinen P, Maki-Paakkanen J, Juutilainen J, Naarala J. **Enhancement of chemically induced reactive oxygen species production and DNA damage in human SH-SY5Y neuroblastoma cells by 872 MHz radiofrequency radiation.** *Mutat Res.* 2009;662:54–58.

n   Mancinelli F, Caraglia M, Abbruzzese A, d'Ambrosio G, Massa R, Bismuto E. **Non-thermal effects of electromagnetic fields at mobile phone frequency on the refolding of an intracellular protein: myoglobin.** *J Cell Biochem.* 2004;93:188–196.

57   Nittby H, Grafström G, Eberhardt JL, et al. **Radiofrequency and extremely low-frequency electro-magnetic field effects on the blood-brain barrier.** *Electromagn Biol Med.* 2008;27(2):103-126.

58   Stam R. **Electromagnetic fields and the blood-brain barrier.** *Brain Res Rev.* 2010. 65(1):80-97. [Epub 2010 Jun 13].

59   Tore F, Dulou P-E, et al. **Two-hour exposure to 2-W/kg, 900-MHZ GSM microwaves induces plasma protein extravasation in rat brain and dura matter.** In: *Proc 5th Int'l Congr EBEA.* Finland, Helsinki. 2001. Pages 43–45.

     Tore F, Dulou P-E, et al. **Effect of 2 hour GSM-900 microwave exposures from 2.0, 0.5 and 0.12 W/kg on plasma protein extravasation in rat brain and dura mater.** In: *Proc 24th Ann Meeting of the BEMS.* 2002. Pages 61–62.

     Persson B RR, Eberhardt J, Malmgren L, et al. **Progress Effects of microwaves from GSM mobile phones on the blood-brain barrier and neurons in rat brain.** In: *Electromagnetics Research Symposium 2005,* Hangzhou, China, August 22-26, 2005. Available from: www.piers.org/piersonline/vol1/2k5hz_p638.pdf.

60   Salford LG, Brun AE, Eberhardt JL, Malmgren L, Persson BR. **Nerve cell damage in mammalian brain after exposure to microwaves from GSM mobile phones.** *Environ Health Perspect.* 2003;111(7):881-883; discussion A408.

61   Eberhardt JL, Persson BR, Brun AE, Salford LG, Malmgren LO. **Blood-brain barrier permeability and nerve cell damage in rat brain 14 and 28 days after exposure to microwaves from GSM mobile phones.** *Electromagn Biol Med.* 2008;27(3):215-229. Abstract only.

     Nittby H, Brun A, Eberhardt J, Malmgren L, Persson BR, Salford LG. **Increased blood-brain barrier permeability in mammalian brain 7 days after exposure to the radiation from a GSM-900 mobile phone.** *Pathophysiology.* 2009;16(2-3):103-112. [Epub 2009 Apr 2].

62   Tang J, Zhang Y, Yang L, et al. **Exposure to 900 MHz electromagnetic fields activates the mkp-1/ERK pathway and causes blood-brain barrier damage and cognitive impairment in rats.** *Brain Res.* 2015;1601:92-101. doi: 10.1016/j.brainres.2015.01.019. [Epub 2015 Jan 15].

63   Mast Sanity website. **Experiments with Cress [and Wi-Fi] in 9th Grade attracts international attention [Denmark] 16th May 2013.** Retrieved August 1, 2015 from: http://mastsanity.org/health-52/research/324-experiments-with-cress-in-9th-grade-attracts-international-attention-denmark-16th-may-2013.html

64   Tuengler A, von Klitzing L. **Hypothesis on how to measure electromagnetic hypersensitivity.** *Electromagn Biol Med.* 2013 Jan 9. [Epub ahead of print].

65   Juutilainen J, Höytö A, Kumlin T, Naarala J. **Review of possible modulation-dependent biological effects of radiofrequency fields.** *Bioelectromagnetics.* 2011;32(7):511-534. Cited in: Tuengler A, von Klitzing L. Hypothesis on how to measure electromagnetic hypersensitivity. Electromagn Biol Med. 2013 Jan 9. [Epub ahead of print].

Laurence JA, French PW, Lindner RA, McKenzie DR. **Biological effects of electromagnetic fields-mechanisms for the effects of pulsed microwave radiation on protein conformation.** *Journal of Theoretical Biology.* 2000;206(2):291-298. Cited in: Tuengler A, von Klitzing L. Hypothesis on how to measure electromagnetic hypersensitivity. Electromagn Biol Med. 2013 Jan 9. [Epub ahead of print].

Gutzeit HO. **Interaction of stressors and the limits of cellular homeostasis.** *Biochemical and Biophysical Research Communications.* 2001;283(4):721-725. Cited in: Tuengler A, von Klitzing L. Hypothesis on how to measure electromagnetic hypersensitivity. Electromagn Biol Med. 2013 Jan 9. [Epub ahead of print].

66 Tuengler A, von Klitzing L. **Hypothesis on how to measure electromagnetic hypersensitivity.** *Electromagn Biol Med.* 2013 Jan 9. [Epub ahead of print].

67 Conrad R. Maine Coalition to Stop Smart Meters. **Smart meter health effects survey & report.** Retrieved July 8, 2015 from: www.conradbiologic.com/smartmetersurvey.html

68 Spirit of Health website. **The Effect of Cell Phone Radiation on the Red Blood Cell.** Retrieved July 12, 2015 from: www.spiritofhealthkc.com/wp/wp-content/uploads/2014/03/CELLPHONES3-The-Effect-of-Cell-Phone-Radiation-on-the-Red-.pdf

Buergerwelle website. **Live blood analysis.** Retrieved July 12, 2015 from: www.buergerwelle.de/assets/files/cluster.jpg?cultureKey=&q=pdf/cluster.jpg

69 Ruan P, Yong J, Shen H, Zheng X. **Monitoring dynamic reactions of red blood cells to UHF electromagnetic waves radiation using a novel micro-imaging technology.** *Electromagn Biol Med.* 2012;31(4):365-374. doi: 10.3109/15368378.2012.662195. [Epub 2012 Jun 7].

70 Frey AH. **Headaches from cellular telephones: are they real and what are the implications?** *Environ Health Perspect.* 1998;106(3):101-103.

71 Safeukui I, Buffet PA, Deplaine G, et al. **Quantitative assessment of sensing and sequestration of spherocytic erythrocytes by the human spleen.** *Blood.* 2012;120(2):424-430. doi: 10.1182/blood-2012-01-404103. [Epub 2012 Apr 17].

72 Web MD website. **Understanding anemia - symptoms.** Retrieved June 30, 2015 from: www.webmd.com/a-to-z-guides/understanding-anemia-symptoms

73 Devrim E, Ergüder IB, Kılıçoğlu B, Yaykaşlı E, Cetin R, Durak I. **Effects of Electromagnetic Radiation Use on Oxidant/Antioxidant Status and DNA Turn-over Enzyme Activities in Erythrocytes and Heart, Kidney, Liver, and Ovary Tissues From Rats: Possible Protective Role of Vitamin C.** *Toxicol Mech Methods.* 2008;18(9):679-683. doi: 10.1080/15376510701380182.

74 El-Bediwi AB, Saad M, El-Kott AF, Eid E. **Influence of electromagnetic radiation produced by mobile phone on some biophysical blood properties in rats.** *Cell Biochem Biophys.* 2012 Oct 10. [Epub ahead of print].

75 Sarookhani MR, Safari A, Zahedpanah M, Ziaeiha M. **Effects of 950 MHz mobile phone electromagnetic fields on the peripheral blood cells of male rabbits.** *African Journal of Pharmacy and Pharmacology.* 2012;6(5):300-304.

76 Lewicka M, Henrykowska GA, Pacholski K, et al. **The effect of electromagnetic radiation emitted by display screens on cell oxygen metabolism - in vitro studies.** *Arch Med Sci.* 2015;11(6):1330-1339. doi: 10.5114/aoms.2015.56362. Epub 2015 Dec 11.

77 Kabuto M, Nitta H, Yamamoto S, et al. **Childhood leukemia and magnetic fields in Japan: a case-control study of childhood leukemia and residential power-frequency magnetic fields in Japan.** *Int J Cancer.* 2006;119(3):643-650.

Feizi AA, Arabi MA. **Acute childhood leukemias and exposure to magnetic fields generated by high voltage overhead power lines – a risk factor in Iran.** *Asian Pac J Cancer Prev.* 2007;8(1):69-72.

Continued on next page

Sohrabi MR, Tarjoman T, Abadi A, Yavari P. **Living near overhead high voltage transmission power lines as a risk factor for childhood acute lymphoblastic leukemia: a case-control study.** *Asian Pac J Cancer Prev.* 2010;11(2):423-427.

78 Schmid MR, Loughran SP, Regel SJ, et al. **Sleep EEG alterations: effects of different pulse-modulated radio frequency electromagnetic fields.** *J Sleep Res.* 2012;21(1):50-58. doi: 10.1111/j.1365-2869.2011.00918.x. [Epub 2011 Apr 12].

79 Schmid MR, Loughran SP, Regel SJ, et al. **Sleep EEG alterations: effects of different pulse-modulated radio frequency electromagnetic fields.** *J Sleep Res.* 2012;21(1):50-58. doi: 10.1111/j.1365-2869.2011.00918.x. [Epub 2011 Apr 12].

80 Pelletier A, Delanaud S, Décima P, et al. **Effects of chronic exposure to radiofrequency electromagnetic fields on energy balance in developing rats.** *Environ Sci Pollut Res Int.* 2012 Nov 10. [Epub ahead of print].

81 Simkó M, Mattsson MO. **Extremely low frequency electromagnetic fields as effectors of cellular responses in vitro: possible immune cell activation.** *J Cell Biochem.* 2004;93(1):83-92.

82 Kumar S, Behari J, Sisodia R. **Impact of microwave at X-band in the aetiology of male infertility.** *Electromagn Biol Med.* 2012;31(3):223-232. doi: 10.3109/15368378.2012.700293.

83 Ekmekcioglu C. **Melatonin receptors in humans: biological role and clinical relevance.** *Biomed Pharmacother.* 2006;60(3):97-108. [Epub 2006 Feb 20].

84 Andrzejak R, Poreba R, Poreba M, et. al. **The influence of the call with a mobile phone on heart rate variability parameters in healthy volunteers.** *Ind Health.* 2008;46(4):409-417.

85 Merriam-webster dictionary website. **Holter monitor.** Retrieved March 8, 2015 from: www.merriam-webster.com/medical/holter%20monitor

86 Yılmaz D, Yıldız M. **Analysis of the mobile phone effect on the heart rate variability by using the largest Lyapunov exponent.** *J Med Syst.* 2010;34(6):1097-1103. doi: 10.1007/s10916-009-9328-z. [Epub 2009 Jun 18].

87 Gangi S, Johansson O. **A theoretical model based upon mast cells and histamine to explain the recently proclaimed sensitivity to electric and/or magnetic fields in humans.** *Med Hypotheses.* 2000;54(4):663-671.

88 Braune S, Wrocklage C, Raczek J, Gailus T, Lücking CH. **Resting blood pressure increase during exposure to a radio-frequency electromagnetic field.** *Lancet.* 1998;351(9119):1857-1858.

89 Paul B, Saha I, Kumar S, Samim Ferdows SK, Ghose G. **Mobile phones: time to rethink and limit usage.** *Indian J Public Health.* 2015;59(1):37-41. doi: 10.4103/0019-557X.152856.

90 Sonmez OF, Odaci E, Bas O, Kaplan S. **Purkinje cell number decreases in the adult female rat cerebellum following exposure to 900 MHz electromagnetic field.** *Brain Res.* 2010;1356:95-101. [Epub 2010 Aug 4].

91 Raqbetli MC, Aydinlioqlu A, Koyun N, Ragbetli C, Bektas S, Ozdemir S. **The effect of mobile phone on the number of Purkinje cells: a stereological study.** *Int J Radiat Biol.* 2010;86(7):548-554.

92 Haghani M, Shabani M, Moazzami K. **Maternal mobile phone exposure adversely affects the electrophysiological properties of Purkinje neurons in rat offspring.** *Neuroscience.* 2013;250:588-598. doi: 10.1016/j.neuroscience.2013.07.049. [Epub 2013 Jul 29].

93 Encyclopedia Britannica website. **Purkinje cell.** Retrieved March 11, 2013 from: www.britannica.com/EBchecked/topic/484088/Purkinje-cell.

94 Ratcliffe R. **Children can swipe a screen but can't use toy building blocks, teachers warn.** *The Guardian* UK news. Tuesday 15 April 2014 13.13 EDT.

95 Integrative Psychiatry website. **Natural GABA (gamma-aminobutyric acid).** Retrieved March 20, 2013 from: www.integrativepsychiatry.net/natural_gaba.html

Edden RA, Crocetti D, Zhu H, Gilbert DL, Mostofsky SH. **Reduced GABA concentration in attention-deficit/hyperactivity disorder.** *Arch Gen Psychiatry.* 2012;69(7):750-753. doi: 10.1001/archgenpsychiatry.2011.2280.

96 Divan HA, Kheifets L, Obel C, Olsen J. **Prenatal and postnatal exposure to cell phone use and behavioral problems in children.** *Epidemiology.* 2008;19(4):523-529. Abstract only.

97 Divan HA, Kheifets L, Obel C, Olsen J. **Cell phone use and behavioural problems in young children.** *J Epidemiol Community Health.* 2012;66(6):524-529. doi: 10.1136/jech.2010.115402. [Epub 2010 Dec 7].

98 Khurana VG, Hardell L, Everaert J, Bortkiewicz A, Carlberg M, Ahonen M. **Epidemiological evidence for a health risk from mobile phone base stations.** *Int J Occup Environ Health.* 2010;16(3):263-267.

99 Han S, Tai C, Westenbroek RE, et al. **Nature Autistic-like behaviour in Scn1a+/- mice and rescue by enhanced GABA-mediated neurotransmission.** *Nature.* 2012;489(7416):385-390. doi: 10.1038/nature11356. [Epub 2012 Aug 22].

Yu FH, Mantegazza M, Westenbroek RE, et al. **Nat Reduced sodium current in GABAergic interneurons in a mouse model of severe myoclonic epilepsy in infancy.** *Neurosci.* 2006;9(9):1142-1149. [Epub 2006 Aug 20].

Chao HT, Chen H, Samaco RC, et al. **Nature Dysfunction in GABA signaling mediates autism-like stereotypies and Rett syndrome phenotypes.** *Nature.* 2010;468(7321):263-269. doi: 10.1038/nature09582.

100 Middleton JW, Kiritani T, Pedersen C, Turner JG, Shepherd GM, Tzounopoulos T. **Mice with behavioral evidence of tinnitus exhibit dorsal cochlear nucleus hyperactivity because of decreased GABAergic inhibition.** *Proc Natl Acad Sci USA.* 2011;108(18):7601-7606. doi: 10.1073/pnas.1100223108. [Epub 2011 Apr 18].

101 Hutter HP, Moshammer H, Wallner P, et al. **Tinnitus and mobile phone use.** *Occup Environ Med.* 2010. 67(12):804-808. doi: 10.1136/oem.2009.048116. [Epub 2010 Jun 23].

102 Uloziene I, Uloza V, Gradauskiene E, Saferis V. **Assessment of potential effects of the electromagnetic fields of mobile phones on hearing.** *BMC Public Health.* 2005;5:39.

103 Stefanics G, Kellényi L, Molnár F, Kubinyi G, Thuróczy G, Hernádi I. **Short GSM mobile phone exposure does not alter human auditory brainstem response.** *BMC Public Health.* 2007;:325.

104 Arai N, Enomoto H, Okabe S, Yuasa K, Kamimura Y, Ugawa Y. **Thirty minutes mobile phone use has no short-term adverse effects on central auditory pathways.** *Clin Neurophysiol.* 2003;114(8):1390-1394.

105 Oktay MF, Dasdag S. **Effects of intensive and moderate cellular phone use on hearing function.** *Electromagn Biol Med.* 2006;25(1):13-21.

106 Velayutham P, Govindasamy GK, Raman R, Prepageran N, Ng KH. **High-frequency hearing loss among mobile phone users.** *Indian J Otolaryngol Head Neck Surg.* 2014;66(Suppl 1):169-172. doi: 10.1007/s12070-011-0406-4. [Epub 2011 Dec 15].

107 Panda NK, Jain R, Bakshi J, Munjal S. **Audiologic disturbances in long-term mobile phone users.** *J Otolaryngol Head Neck Surg.* 2010;39(1):5-11.

108 Kaprana AE, Chimona TS, Papadakis CE, et al. **Auditory brainstem response changes during exposure to GSM-900 radiation: an experimental study.** *Audiol Neurootol.* 2011;16(4):270-276. doi: 10.1159/000321337. [Epub 2010 Nov 16].

109 Khullar S, Sood A, Sood S. **Auditory Brainstem Responses and EMFs Generated by Mobile Phones.** *Indian J Otolaryngol Head Neck Surg.* 2013;65(Suppl 3):645-649. doi: 10.1007/s12070-013-0676-0. [Epub 2013 Sep 7].

110 Lipman RM, Tripathi BJ, Tripathi RC. **Cataracts induced by microwave and ionizing radiation.** *Surv Ophthalmol.* 1988;33(3):200-210.

111 Bormusov E, P Andley U, Sharon N, Schächter L, Lahav A, Dovrat A. **Non-thermal electromagnetic radiation damage to lens epithelium.** *Open Ophthalmol J.* 2008;2:102-106. doi: 10.2174/1874364100802010102.

112 Balci M, Devrim E, Durak I. **Effects of mobile phones on oxidant/antioxidant balance in cornea and lens of rats.** *Curr Eye Res.* 2007;32(1):21-25.

113 Balci M, Namuslu M, Devrim E, Durak I. **Effects of computer monitor-emitted radiation on oxidant/antioxidant balance in cornea and lens from rats.** *Mol Vis.* 2009;15:2521-2525.

114 Yang L, Ge M, Guo J, Wang Q, Jiang X, Yan W. **A simulation for effects of RF electromagnetic radiation from a mobile handset on eyes model using the finite-difference time-domain method.** *Conf Proc IEEE Eng Med Biol Soc.* 2007. 2007;5294-5297.

115 Roux D, Vian A, Girard S, et al. **High frequency (900 MHz) low amplitude (5 V m-1) electromagnetic field: a genuine environmental stimulus that affects transcription, translation, calcium and energy charge in tomato.** *Planta.* 2008;227(4):883-891. [Epub 2007 Nov 20].

116 Maskey D, Kim M, Aryal B, et al. **Effect of 835 MHz radiofrequency radiation exposure on calcium binding proteins in the hippocampus of the mouse brain.** *Brain Res.* 2010;1313:232-341. doi: 10.1016/j.brainres.2009.11.079. [Epub 2009 Dec 5].

117 Celikozlu SD, Ozyurt MS, Cimbiz A, Yardimoglu MY, Cayci MK, Ozay Y. **The effects of long term exposure of magnetic field via 900-MHz GSM radiation on some biochemical parameters and brain histology in rats.** *Electromagn Biol Med.* 2012;31(4):344-355. doi: 10.3109/15368378.2012.662192. [Epub 2012 Jun 7].

118 Irmak MK, Fadillioglu E, Gulec M, et. al. **Effects of electromagnetic radiation from a cellular telephone on the oxidant and antioxidant levels in rabbits.** *Cell Biochemistry and Function.* 2002;20(4):279–283.

119 Caprani A, Richert A, Flaud P. **Experimental evidence of a potentially increased thrombo-embolic disease risk by domestic electromagnetic field exposure.** *Bioelectromagnetics.* 2004;25(4):313-315.

120 World Heart Federation website. **Stroke and blood clots.** Retrieved July 13, 2015 from: www.world-heart-federation.org/cardiovascular-health/stroke/stroke-and-blood-clots/

121 Kissela BM, Khoury JC, Alwell K, Moomaw CJ, et al. **Age at stroke: temporal trends in stroke incidence in a large, biracial population.** *Neurology.* 2012;79(17):1781-1787. doi: 10.1212/WNL.0b013e318270401d. [Epub 2012 Oct 10].

122 BBC News website. **Strokes rising among people of working age, warns charity.** Retrieved June 1, 2015 from: www.bbc.com/news/health-32690040

123 Bikle DD, Oda Y, Xie Z. **Calcium and 1,25(OH)2D: interacting drivers of epidermal differentiation.** *J Steroid Biochem Mol Biol.* 2004y;89-90(1-5):355-360.

124 Rajkovic V, Matavulj M, Johansson O. **Combined exposure of peripubertal male rats to the endocrine-disrupting compound atrazine and power-frequency electromagnetic fields causes degranulation of cutaneous mast cells: a new toxic environmental hazard?** *Arch Environ Contam Toxicol.* 2010;59(2):334-341. doi: 10.1007/s00244-010-9477-6. [Epub 2010 Feb 11].

125 Scott RS, Clay L, Storey KV, Johnson RJ. **Transient microwave induced neurosensory reactions during superficial hyperthermia treatment.** *Int J Radiat Oncol Biol Phys.* 1985;11(3):561-566.

126 Westerman R, Hocking B. **Diseases of modern living: neurological changes associated with mobile phones and radiofrequency radiation in humans.** *Neurosci Lett.* 2004;361(1-3):13-16.

127 Redmayne M, Johansson O. **Could myelin damage from radiofrequency electromagnetic field exposure help explain the functional impairment electrohypersensitivity? A review of the evidence.** *J Toxicol Environ Health B Crit Rev.* 2014;17(5):247-258. doi: 10.1080/10937404.2014.923356.

128 Huttunen P, Savinainen A, Hänninen O, Myllylä R. **Involuntary human hand movements due to FM radio waves in a moving van.** *Acta Physiol Hung.* 2011;98(2):157-164. doi: 10.1556/APhysiol.98.2011.2.7.

129 Huttunen P, Hänninen O, Myllylä R. **FM-radio and TV tower signals can cause spontaneous hand movements near moving RF reflector.** *Pathophysiology.* 2009;16(2-3):201-204. doi: 10.1016/j.pathophys.2009.01.002. [Epub 2009 Mar 5].

130 CT Government website. **Infectious Diseases.** Retrieved February 1, 2016 from: www.ct.gov/dph/lib/dph/infectious_diseases/lyme/1976_circular_letter.pdf

131 Abdel-Rassoul G, El-Fateh OA, Salem MA, Michael A, Farahat F, El-Batanouny M, Salem E. **Neurobehavioral effects among inhabitants around mobile phone base stations.** *Neurotoxicology.* 2007;28(2):434-440. Epub 2006 Aug 1.

132 Lyme Disease Research Database (LDRD) website. **Lyme Disease Tests.** Retrieved February 7, 2016 from: www.lyme-disease-research-database.com/lyme_disease_tests.html

133 Belpomme D, Campagnac C, Irigaray P. **Reliable disease biomarkers characterizing and identifying electrohypersensitivity and multiple chemical sensitivity as two etiopathogenic aspects of a unique pathological disorder.** *Rev Environ Health.* 2015;30(4):251-271. doi: 10.1515/reveh-2015-0027.

134 Rolls ET. **Neurophysiology and cognitive functions of the striatum.** *Rev Neurol* (Paris). 1994;150(8-9):648-660.

135 Oscar KJ, Gruenau SP, Folker MT, Rapoport SI. **Local cerebral blood flow after microwave exposure.** *Brain Res.* 1981;204(1):220-225.

136 Wordnik Dictionary website. **Definition astrogliosis.** Retrieved April 5, 2015 from: www.wordnik.com/words/astrogliosis

137 Medicine Net website. **Definition gliosis.** Retrieved April 5, 2015 from: www.medicinenet.com/script/main/art.asp?articlekey=25457

138 Wikipedia website. **Definition glial fibrillary acidic protein (GFAP).** Retrieved September 16, 2015 from: https://en.wikipedia.org/wiki/Glial_fibrillary_acidic_protein

139 Ammari M, Gamez C, Lecomte A, Sakly M, Abdelmelek H, De Seze R. **GFAP expression in the rat brain following sub-chronic exposure to a 900 MHz electromagnetic field signal.** *Int J Radiat Biol.* 2010;86(5):367-375. doi: 10.3109/09553000903567946.

140 Eser O, Songur A, Aktas C, et. al. **The effect of electromagnetic radiation on the rat brain: an experimental study.** *Turk Neurosurg.* 2013;23(6):707-715. doi: 10.5137/1019-5149.JTN.7088-12.2.

141 Aalto S, Haarala C, Bruck A, Sipila H, Hamalainen H, Rinne JO. **Mobile phone affects cerebral blood flow in humans.** *J Cereb Blood Flow Metab.* 2006;26:885–890. Abstract only.

142 de Tommaso M, Rossi P, Falsaperla R, Francesco VdeV, Santoro R, Federici A. **Mobile phones exposure induces changes of contingent negative variation in humans.** *Neurosci Lett.* 2009;464(2):79-83. [Epub 2009 Aug 21].

143 Partsvania B, Sulaberidze T, Shoshiashvili L. **Effect of high SARs produced by cell phone like radio-frequency fields on mollusk single neuron.** *Electromagn Biol Med.* 2013;32(1):48-58. doi: 10.3109/15368378.2012.701190. [Epub 2012 Oct 9].

144 Kesari KK, Kumar S, Behari J. **Pathophysiology of microwave radiation: effect on rat brain.** *Appl Biochem Biotechnol.* 2012;166(2):379-388. doi: 10.1007/s12010-011-9433-6. [Epub 2011 Nov 29].

145 Volkow ND, Tomasi D, Wang GJ, et al. **Effects of cell phone radiofrequency signal exposure on brain glucose metabolism.** *JAMA.* 2011;305(8):808-813.

146 Kwon MS, Vorobyev V, Kännälä S, et al. **GSM mobile phone radiation suppresses brain glucose metabolism.** *J Cereb Blood Flow Metab.* 2011;31(12):2293-2301. doi: 10.1038/jcbfm.2011.128. [Epub 2011 Sep 14].

147 Eichenbaum H. **What H.M. (sometimes referred to as Henry M.) taught us.** *J Cogn Neurosci.* 2013;25(1):14-21. doi: 10.1162/jocn_a_00285. [Epub 2012 Aug 20].
    Costandi M [personal blog]. **Remembering Henry M.** Science Blogs website. Retrieved January 10, 2013 from: http://scienceblogs.com/neurophilosophy/2007/07/28/remembering-henry-m/.
    Tulving E, Markowitsch HJ. **Episodic and declarative memory: Role of the hippocampus.** *Hippocampus.* 1998;8(3):198-204.
148 Odaci E, Bas O, Kaplan S. **Effects of prenatal exposure to a 900 MHz electromagnetic field on the dentate gyrus of rats: a stereological and histopathological study.** *Brain Res.* 2008;1238:224-229. [Epub 2008 Aug 16].
149 Kamphuis W, Middeldorp J, Kooijman L, et al. **Glial fibrillary acidic protein isoform expression in plaque related astrogliosis in Alzheimer's disease.** *Neurobiol Aging.* 2014;35(3):492-510. doi: 10.1016/j.neurobiolaging.2013.09.035. [Epub 2013 Oct 23].
150 Nittby H, Grafström G, Tian DP. **Cognitive impairment in rats after long-term exposure to GSM-900 mobile phone radiation.** *Bioelectromagnetics.* 2008;29(3):219-232.
151 Tang J, Zhang Y, Yang L, et al. **Exposure to 900 MHz electromagnetic fields activates the mkp-1/ERK pathway and causes blood-brain barrier damage and cognitive impairment in rats.** *Brain Res.* 2015;1601: 92-101. doi: 10.1016/j.brainres.2015.01.019. [Epub 2015 Jan 15].
152 Prut L, Prenosil G, Willadt S, Vogt K, Fritschy JM, Crestani F. **A reduction in hippocampal GABAA receptor alpha5 subunits disrupts the memory for location of objects in mice.** *Genes Brain Behav.* 2010;9(5):478-488. doi: 10.1111/j.1601-183X.2010.00575.x. [Epub 2010 Feb 17].
153 Gueli MC, Taibi G. **Alzheimer's disease: amino acid levels and brain metabolic status.** *Neurol Sci.* 2013. [Epub ahead of print].
154 Chang Q, He Y, Ni B, Feng K, Jiang Y, Jiang B. **A case-control study on the risk factors of Alzheimer's disease in military elderly men.** *Zhonghua Liu Xing Bing Xue Za Zhi.* 2004;25(10):890-893.
155 Harmanci H, Emre M, Gurvit H, et al. **Risk factors for Alzheimer disease: a population-based case-control study in Istanbul, Turkey.** *Alzheimer Dis Assoc Disord.* 2003;17(3):139-145.
156 Sobel E, Dunn M, Davanipour Z, Davanipour Z, Qian Z, Chui HC. **Elevated risk of Alzheimer's disease among workers with likely electromagnetic field exposure.** *Neurology.* 1996;47(6):1477-1481.
157 Savitz DA, Loomis DP, Tse CK. **Electrical occupations and neurodegenerative disease: analysis of U.S. mortality data.** *Arch Environ Health.* 1998;53(1):71-74.
158 Balaguru S, Uppal R, Vaid RP, Kumar BP. **Investigation of the spinal cord as a natural receptor antenna for incident electromagnetic waves and possible impact on the central nervous system.** *Electromagn Biol Med.* 2012;31(2):101-111. doi: 10.3109/15368378.2011.624653. [Epub 2012 Feb 21].
159 Söderqvist F, Carlberg M, Hardell L. **Mobile and cordless telephones, serum transthyretin and the blood-cerebrospinal fluid barrier: a cross-sectional study.** *Environ Health.* 2009;8:19. doi: 10.1186/1476-069X-8-19.
160 Science Daily website. **Multiple sclerosis is increasingly becoming a woman's disease: why?** Retrieved March 14, 2013 from: www.sciencedaily.com¬/releases/2007/04/070427072325.htm
161 Minagar A, Jy W, Jimenez JJ, Alexander JS. **Multiple sclerosis as a vascular disease.** *Neurol Res.* 2006;28(3):230-235.
162 Kirk J, Plumb J, Mirakhur M, McQuaid S. **Tight junctional abnormality in multiple sclerosis white matter affects all calibres of vessel and is associated with blood-brain barrier leakage and active demyelination.** *J Pathol.* 2003;201(2):319-327.

Salford LG, Brun AE, Eberhardt JL, Malmgren L, Persson BR. **Nerve cell damage in mammalian brain after exposure to microwaves from GSM mobile phones.** *Environ Health Perspect.* 2003;111(7):881-883; discussion A408.

Eberhardt JL, Persson BR, Brun AE, Salford LG, Malmgren LO. **Blood-brain barrier permeability and nerve cell damage in rat brain 14 and 28 days after exposure to microwaves from GSM mobile phones.** *Electromagn Biol Med.* 2008;27(3):215-229. Abstract only.

Nittby H, Brun A, Eberhardt J, Malmgren L, Persson BR, Salford LG. **Increased blood-brain barrier permeability in mammalian brain 7 days after exposure to the radiation from a GSM-900 mobile phone.** *Pathophysiology.* 2009;16(2-3):103-112. [Epub 2009 Apr 2].

Tang J, Zhang Y, Yang L, et al. **Exposure to 900 MHz electromagnetic fields activates the mkp-1/ERK pathway and causes blood-brain barrier damage and cognitive impairment in rats.** *Brain Res.* 2015;1601:92-101. doi: 10.1016/j.brainres.2015.01.019. [Epub 2015 Jan 15].

163 Minagar A, Jy W, Jimenez JJ, Alexander JS. **Multiple sclerosis as a vascular disease.** *Neurol Res.* 2006;28(3):230-235.

Leech S, Kirk J, Plumb J, McQuaid S. **Persistent endothelial abnormalities and blood-brain barrier leak in primary and secondary progressive multiple sclerosis.** *Neuropathol Appl Neurobiol.* 2007;33(1):86-98.

Minagar A, Maghzi AH, McGee JC, Alexander JS. **Emerging roles of endothelial cells in multiple sclerosis pathophysiology and therapy.** *Neurol Res.* 2012;34(8):738-745. doi: 10.1179/1743132812Y.0000000072. [Epub 2012 Jul 23].

164 Mortazavi SMJ, Daiee E, Yazdi A, et al. **Mercury release from dental amalgam restorations after magnetic resonance imaging and following mobile phone use.** *Pakistan Journal of Biological Science.* 2008;11: 1142-1146.

165 Godfrey ME, Wojcik DP, Krone CA. **Apolipoprotein E genotyping as a potential biomarker for mercury neurotoxicity.** *J Alzheimers Dis.* 2003;5(3):189-195.

166 MercuryTalk website. **Mercury Excretion and APO-E 4/3 4/4 Genotypes.** Retrieved July 9, 2015 from: http://mercurytalk.com/articles/Mercury-Excretion-and-APO-E-Genotypes.html#.VZ7ryBy6LYE

167 Siblerud RL, Kienholz E. **Evidence that mercury from silver dental fillings may be an etiological factor in multiple sclerosis.** *Sci Total Environ.* 1994;142(3):191-205.

168 Rothwell JA, Boyd PJ. **Amalgam dental fillings and hearing loss.** *Int J Audiol.* 2008;47(12):770-776. doi: 10.1080/14992020802311224

Mortada WL, Sobh MA, El-Defrawy MM, Farahat SE. **Mercury in dental restoration: is there a risk of nephrotoxicity?** *J Nephrol.* 2002;15(2):171-176.

169 Pugliatti M, Riise T, Sotgiu MA, et al. **Increasing incidence of multiple sclerosis in the province of Sassari, northern Sardinia.** *Neuroepidemiology.* 2005;25(3):129-134. [Epub 2005 Jun 29].

170 Pugliatti M, Cossu P, Sotgiu S, Rosati G, Riise T. **Clustering of multiple sclerosis, age of onset and gender in Sardinia.** *J Neurol Sci.* 2009;286(1-2):6-13. Doi: 10.1016/j.jns.2009.07.013. [Epub 2009 Aug 11].

171 Grytten N, Torkildsen Ø, Myhr K, M. **Time trends in the incidence and prevalence of multiple sclerosis in Norway during eight decades.** *Acta Neurologica Scandinavica. Special Issue: Nordic MS Epidemiology.* 2015;132(Supp S199): 29–36. DOI: 10.1111/ane.12428.

172 Patel JP, Frey BN. **Disruption in the blood-brain barrier: The missing link between brain and body inflammation in bipolar disorder?** *Neural Plast.* 2015;2015:708306. [Epub 2015 May 13].

173 Réus GZ, Fries GR, Stertz L, et al. **The role of inflammation and microglial activation in the pathophysiology of psychiatric disorders.** *Neuroscience.* 2015;300:141-154. doi: 10.1016/j.neuroscience.2015.05.018. [Epub 2015 May 14].

174 Moreno C, Laje G, Blanco C, Jiang H, Schmidt AB, Olfson M. **National trends in the outpatient diagnosis and treatment of bipolar disorder in youth.** *Arch Gen Psychiatry.* 2007;64(9):1032-1039.

175 Salehi I, Sani KG, Zamani A. **Exposure of rats to extremely low-frequency electromagnetic fields (ELF-EMF) alters cytokines production.** *Electromagn Biol Med.* 2012 Oct 9. [Epub ahead of print]. Abstract only.

176 Johansson O. **Disturbance of the immune system by electromagnetic fields-a potentially underlying cause for cellular damage and tissue repair reduction which could lead to disease and impairment.** *Pathophysiology.* 2009;16(2-3):157-177. [Epub 2009 Apr 23].

177 Hekmat A, Saboury AA, Moosavi-Movahedi AA. **The toxic effects of mobile phone radiofrequency (940MHz) on the structure of calf thymus DNA.** *Ecotoxicol Environ Saf.* 2013;88:35-41. doi: 10.1016/j.ecoenv.2012.10.016. [Epub 2012 Nov 17].

178 Simkó M. **Induction of cell activation processes by low frequency electromagnetic fields.** *Scientific World Journal.* 2004;4(S2):4–22. ISSN 1537-744X; DOI 10.1100/tsw.2004.174.

      Simkó M, Richard D, Kriehuber R, Weiss DG. **Micronucleus induction in SHE cells following exposure to 50 Hz magnetic fields, benzo(a)pyrene and TPA in vitro.** *Mutat Res.* 2001;495(1-2):43–50.

179 Hervé JC. **The connexins, part III, [editorial].** *Biochimt Biophys Acta.* 2005;1719(1-2):1-2.

      Leithe E, Sirnes S, Omori Y, Rivedal E. **Downregulation of gap junctions in cancer cells.** *Crit Rev Oncog.* 2006;12(3-4):225-256.

180 Yang L, Hao D, Wang M, Zeng Y, Wu S, Zeng Y. **Cellular neoplastic transformation induced by 916 MHz microwave radiation.** *Cell Mol Neurobiol.* 2012;32(6):1039-1046. doi: 10.1007/s10571-012-9821-7. [Epub 2012 Mar 7].

181 Lerchl A, Klose M, Grote K, et al. **Tumor promotion by exposure to radiofrequency electromagnetic fields below exposure limits for humans.** *Biochem Biophys Res Commun.* 2015;459(4):585-590. doi: 10.1016/j.bbrc.2015.02.151. [Epub 2015 Mar 6].

182 Dode AC, Leao M, Tejo FAF, et. al. **Mortality by neoplasia and cellular telephone base stations in the Belo Horizonte municipality, Minas Gerais state, Brazil.** *Sci Total Environ.* 2011;409(19):3649-3665.

183 Foster KR, Trottier L, **Comments on "mortality by neoplasia and cellular telephone base stations in the Belo Horizonte municipality, Minas Gerais state, ...,"** *Sci Total Environ.* (2012), doi: 10.1016/j.scitotenv.2012.06.007

184 Dode AC, Leao M, Tejo FAF. **Comments on "Foster KR, Trottier L, Comments on "mortality by neoplasia and cellular telephone base stations in the Belo Horizonte municipality, Minas Gerais state, ...,"** *Sci Total Environ.* 2013. 442:553-556.

185 Simkó M. **Cell type specific redox status is responsible for diverse electromagnetic field effects.** *Curr Med Chem.* 2007;14(10):1141-1152.

186 Ivancsits S, Diem E, Pilger A, Rüdiger HW, Jahn O. **Induction of DNA strand breaks by intermittent exposure to extremely-low-frequency electromagnetic fields in human diploid fibroblasts.** *Mutat Res.* 2002;519(1-2):1-13.

187 UCLA website. **Glioma definition.** Retrieved March 15, 2015 from: http://neurosurgery.ucla.edu/body.cfm?id=159

188 Wei M, Guizzetti M, Yost M, Costa LG. **Exposure to 60-Hz magnetic fields and proliferation of human astrocytoma cells in vitro.** *Toxicol Appl Pharmacol.* 2000;162(3):166-176.

189 Diem E, Schwarz C, Adlkofer F, Jahn O, Rüdiger H. **Non-thermal DNA breakage by mobile-phone radiation (1800 MHz) in human fibroblasts and in transformed GFSH-R17 rat granulosa cells in vitro.** *Mutat Res.* 2005;583(2):178-183.

190 Vijayalaxmi, McNamee JP, Scarfi MR. **Comments on: "DNA strand breaks" by Diem et al. [Mutat. Res. 583 (2005) 178-183] and Ivancsits et al. [Mutat. Res. 583 (2005) 184-188].** *Mutat Res.* 2006;603(1):104-106; author reply 107-9. [Epub 2005 Dec 27].
   Lerchl A, Wilhelm AF. **Critical comments on DNA breakage by mobile-phone electromagnetic fields [Diem et al., Mutat. Res. 583 (2005) 178-183].** *Mutat Res.* 2010;697(1-2):60-65. doi:
191 Rüdiger HW. **Letter to the editor: doubts raised about the blinding process do not apply to the Diem et al. paper.** *Mutat Res.* 2009;673(1):2. doi: 10.1016/j.mrgentox.2008.11.002. [Epub 2008 Nov 19].
   Baan RA. **Editorial: controversy related to two published papers.** *Mutat Res.* 2009;673(1):1. doi: 10.1016/j.mrgentox.2008.11.003. [Epub 2008 Nov 19]. Comment on: Non-thermal DNA breakage by mobile-phone radiation (1800 MHz) in human fibroblasts and in transformed GFSH-R17 rat granulosa cells in vitro. *Mutat Res.* 2005.
   Baan RA. **Letter of concern. Comment on:Non-thermal DNA breakage by mobile-phone radiation (1800 MHz) in human fibroblasts and in transformed GFSH-R17 rat granulosa cells in vitro. [Mutat Res. 2005].** *Mutat Res.* 2010;695(1-2):1. doi: 10.1016/j.mrgentox.2009.11.004. [Epub 2009 Nov 13].
192 Khurana VG, Teo C, Kundi M, Hardell L, Carlberg M. **Cell phones and brain tumors: a review including the long-term epidemiologic data.** *Surg Neurol.* 2009;72(3):205-514; discussion 214-215. [Epub 2009 Mar 27].
193 Carlberg M, Hardell L. **On the association between glioma, wireless phones, heredity and ionising radiation.** *Pathophysiology.* 2012;19(4):243-252.
194 Hardell L, Carlberg M, Hansson Mild K. **Use of mobile phones and cordless phones is associated with increased risk for glioma and acoustic neuroma.** *Pathophysiology.* 2012 Dec 20. pii: S0928-4680(12)00110-1. doi: 10.1016/j.pathophys.2012.11.001. [Epub ahead of print].
195 Carlberg M, Hardell L. **Decreased survival of glioma patients with astrocytoma grade IV (glioblastoma multiforme) associated with long-term use of mobile and cordless phones.** *Int J Environ Res Public Health.* 2014;11(10):10790-10805. doi: 10.3390/ijerph111010790.
196 Hardell L, Carlberg M. **Mobile phone and cordless phone use and the risk for glioma - Analysis of pooled case-control studies in Sweden, 1997-2003 and 2007-2009.** *Pathophysiology.* 2015;22(1):1-13. doi: 10.1016/j.pathophys.2014.10.001. [Epub 2014 Oct 29].
197 West JG, Kapoor NS, Liao SY, Chen JW, Bailey L, Nagourney RA. **Multifocal breast cancer in young women with prolonged contact between their breasts and their cellular phones.** *Case Rep Med.* 2013;2013:354682. [Epub 2013 Sep 18].
198 Stevens RG, Davis S. **The melatonin hypothesis: electric power and breast cancer.** *Environ Health Perspect.* 1996;104(Suppl 1):135-140.
   Beniashvili DS, Bilanishvili VG, Menabde MZ. **Low-frequency electromagnetic radiation enhances the induction of rat mammary tumors by nitrosomethyl urea.** *Cancer Lett.* 1991;61(1):75-79.
199 Simkó M. **Induction of cell activation processes by low frequency electromagnetic fields.** *Scientific World Journal.* 2004;4(S2):4-22. ISSN 1537-744X; DOI 10.1100/tsw.2004.174.
200 World Health Organization website. **Latest world cancer statistics Global cancer burden rises to 14.1 million new cases in 2012: Marked increase in breast cancers must be addressed.** Retrieved August 4, 2015 from: www.iarc.fr/en/media-centre/pr/2013/pdfs/pr223_E.pdf
201 Ozguner F, Altinbas A, Ozaydin M, et. al. **Mobile phone-induced myocardial oxidative stress: protection by a novel antioxidant agent caffeic acid phenethyl ester.** *Toxicol Ind Health.* 2005;21(9):223-230.

202 Kiray A, Tayefi H, Kiray M, et al. **The effects of exposure to electromagnetic field on rat myocardium.** *Toxicol Ind Health.* 2013;29(5):418-425. doi: 10.1177/0748233711434957. [Epub 2012 Feb 9].

203 Özorak A, Nazıroğlu M, Çelik Ö, et al. **Wi-Fi (2.45 GHz)- and mobile phone (900 and 1800 MHz)-induced risks on oxidative stress and elements in kidney and testis of rats during pregnancy and the development of offspring.** *Biol Trace Elem Res.* 2013;156(1-3):221-229. doi: 10.1007/s12011-013-9836-z. [Epub 2013 Oct 8].

204 Ozguner F1, Oktem F, Ayata A, Koyu A, Yilmaz HR. **A novel antioxidant agent caffeic acid phenethyl ester prevents long-term mobile phone exposure-induced renal impairment in rat. Prognostic value of malondialdehyde, N-acetyl-beta-D-glucosaminidase and nitric oxide determination.** *Mol Cell Biochem.* 2005;277(1-2):73-80.

205 Ozguner F, Oktem F, Armagan A, et. al. **Comparative analysis of the protective effects of melatonin and caffeic acid phenethyl ester (CAPE) on mobile phone-induced renal impairment in rat.** *Mol Cell Biochem.* 2005;276(1-2):31-37.

206 Devrim E, Ergüder IB, Kılıçoğlu B, Yaykaşlı E, Cetin R, Durak I. **Effects of electromagnetic radiation use on oxidant/antioxidant status and dna turn-over enzyme activities in erythrocytes and heart, kidney, liver, and ovary tissues from rats: Possible protective role of vitamin C.** *Toxicol Mech Methods.* 2008;18(9):679-683. doi: 10.1080/15376510701380182.

207 Koca O, Gokce AM, Akyuz M, et. al. **A new problem in inflammatory bladder diseases: use of mobile phones!** *Int Braz J Urol.* 2014;40(4):520-525. doi: 10.1590/S1677-5538.IBJU.2014.04.11.

208 Bikle DD, Oda Y, Xie Z. **Calcium and 1,25(OH)2D: interacting drivers of epidermal differentiation.** *J Steroid Biochem Mol Biol.* 2004;89-90(1-5):355-360.

209 Rajkovic V, Matavulj M, Johansson O. **Combined exposure of peripubertal male rats to the endocrine-disrupting compound atrazine and power-frequency electromagnetic fields causes degranulation of cutaneous mast cells: a new toxic environmental hazard?** *Arch Environ Contam Toxicol.* 2010;59(2):334-341. doi: 10.1007/s00244-010-9477-6. [Epub 2010 Feb 11].

210 Johansson O, Hilliges M, Björnhagen V, Hall K. **Skin changes in patients claiming to suffer from "screen dermatitis": a two-case open-field provocation study.** *Exp Dermatol.* 1994;3(5):234-238.

211 Johansson O, Hilliges M, Han SW. **A screening of skin changes, with special emphasis on neurochemical marker antibody evaluation, in patients claiming to suffer from "screen dermatitis" as compared to normal healthy controls.** *Exp Dermatol.* 1996;5(5):279-285.

212 Gangi S, Johansson O. **Skin changes in "screen dermatitis" versus classical UV- and ionizing irradiation-related damage--similarities and differences.** *Exp Dermatol.* 1997;6(6):283-291

213 Gangi S, Johansson O. **A theoretical model based upon mast cells and histamine to explain the recently proclaimed sensitivity to electric and/or magnetic fields in humans.** *Med Hypotheses.* 2000;54(4):663-671.

214 Johansson O, Gangi S, Liang Y, Yoshimura K, Jing C, Liu PY. **Cutaneous mast cells are altered in normal healthy volunteers sitting in front of ordinary TVs/PCs--results from open-field provocation experiments.** *J Cutan Pathol.* 2001;28(10):513-519.

215 Gschwandtner M, Mildner M, Mlitz V, et al. **Histamine suppresses epidermal keratinocyte differentiation and impairs skin barrier function in a human skin model.** *Allergy.* 2012 Nov 15. doi: 10.1111/all.12051. [Epub ahead of print].

216 Ozguner F, Aydin G, Mollaoglu H, Gökalp O, Koyu A, Cesur G. **Prevention of mobile phone induced skin tissue changes by melatonin in rat: an experimental study.** *Toxicol Ind Health.* 2004;20(6-10):133-139.

217 Bikle DD, Chang S, Crumrine D, et al. **Mice lacking 25OHD 1alpha-hydroxylase demonstrate decreased epidermal differentiation and barrier function.** *J Steroid Biochem Mol Biol.* 2004;89-90(1-5):347-353.

Bikle DD, Oda Y, Xie Z. **Calcium and 1,25(OH)2D: interacting drivers of epidermal differentiation.** *J Steroid Biochem Mol Biol.* 2004;89-90(1-5):355-360.

218 Pasonen-Seppänen S, Suhonen TM, Kirjavainen M, et al. **Vitamin C enhances differentiation of a continuous keratinocyte cell line (REK) into epidermis with normal stratum corneum ultrastructure and functional permeability barrier.** *Histochem Cell Biol.* 2001;116(4):287-297.

219 Roux D, Vian A, Girard S, et al. **High frequency (900 MHz) low amplitude (5 V m-1) electromagnetic field: a genuine environmental stimulus that affects transcription, translation, calcium and energy charge in tomato.** *Planta.* 2008;227(4):883-891. [Epub 2007 Nov 20].

220 Black B, Granja-Vazquez R, Johnston BR, Jones E, Romero-Ortega M. **Anthropogenic Radio-Frequency Electromagnetic Fields Elicit Neuropathic Pain in an Amputation Model.** PLoS One. 2016 Jan 13;11(1):e0144268. doi: 10.1371/journal.pone.0144268. eCollection 2016.

221 Celikozlu SD, Ozyurt MS, Cimbiz A, Yardimoglu MY, Cayci MK, Ozay Y. **The effects of long term exposure of magnetic field via 900-MHz GSM radiation on some biochemical parameters and brain histology in rats.** *Electromagn Biol Med.* 2012;31(4):344-355. doi: 10.3109/15368378.2012.662192. [Epub 2012 Jun 7].

222 Oztas B, Kucuk M. **Influence of acute arterial hypertension on blood-brain barrier permeability in streptozocin-induced diabetic rats.** *Neurosci Lett.* 1995;188(1):53-56.

223 Oztas B, Kalkan T, Tuncel H. **Influence of 50 Hz frequency sinusoidal magnetic field on the blood-brain barrier permeability of diabetic rats.** *Bioelectromagnetics.* 2004;25(5):400-402.

224 Havas M. **Dirty electricity elevates blood sugar among electrically sensitive diabetics and may explain brittle diabetes.** *Electromagn Biol Med.* 2008;27(2):135-146. doi: 10.1080/15368370802072075.

225 National Institutes of Health (U.S.) website. **Classification of Overweight and Obesity by BMI, Waist Circumference, and Associated Disease Risks.** Retrieved July 13, 2015 from: www.nhlbi.nih.gov/health/educational/lose_wt/BMI/bmi_dis.htm.

226 Geldenhuys S, Hart PH, Endersby R. **Ultraviolet radiation suppresses obesity and symptoms of metabolic syndrome independently of vitamin D in mice fed a high-fat diet.** *Diabetes.* 2014 Nov;63(11):3759-3769. doi: 10.2337/db13-1675.

227 BBC News website. **Skin cancers rates "surge since 1970s."** Retrieved March 16, 2015 from: www.bbc.com/news/health-27065916

228 Purdue MP, Freeman LEB, Anderson WF, Tucker MA. **Recent trends in incidence of cutaneous melanoma among US Caucasian young adults.** *Journ Invest Dermatol.* 2008; 128:2905-2908; doi:10.1038/jid.2008.159; published online 10 July 2008. Last checked June 4, 2014.

U.S. Cancer Statistics Working Group. **United States Cancer Statistics: 1999–2011 Incidence and Mortality Web-based Report.** Atlanta (GA): Department of Health and Human Services, Centers for Disease Control and Prevention, and National Cancer Institute; 2014.

229 Hallberg O, Johansson O. **Malignant melanoma of the skin - not a sunshine story!** *Med Sci Monit.* 2004;10(7):CR336-340. [Epub 2004 Jun 29].

230 Garland CF, Garland FC, Gorham ED. **Rising trends in melanoma. An hypothesis concerning sunscreen effectiveness.** *Ann Epidemiol.* 1993;3(1):103-110.

231 Wu Q, Clark MS, Palmiter RD. **Deciphering a neuronal circuit that mediates appetite.** *Nature.* 2012;14;483(7391):594-597. doi: 10.1038/nature10899.
     Wu Q, Palmiter RD. **GABAergic signaling by AgRP neurons prevents anorexia via a melanocortin-independent mechanism.** *Eur J Pharmacol.* 2011;660(1):21-27. doi: 10.1016/j.ejphar.2010.10.110. [Epub 2011 Jan 3].
     Wu Q, Boyle MP, Palmiter RD. **Loss of GABAergic signaling by AgRP neurons to the parabrachial nucleus leads to starvation.** *Cell.* 2009;137(7):1225-1234. doi: 10.1016/j.cell.2009.04.022.
232 Barbarich-Marsteller NC, Fornal CA, Takase LF, et al. **Activity-based anorexia is associated with reduced hippocampal cell proliferation in adolescent female rats.** *Behav Brain Res.* 2013;236(1):251-257. doi: 10.1016/j.bbr.2012.08.047. [Epub 2012 Sep 4].
233 Nazıroğlu M, Yüksel M, Köse SA, Özkaya MO. **Recent reports of Wi-Fi and mobile phone-induced radiation on oxidative stress and reproductive signaling pathways in females and males.** *J Membr Biol.* 2013;246(12):869-875. [Epub 2013 Oct 9].
234 Gye MC, Park CJ. **Effect of electromagnetic field exposure on the reproductive system.** *Clin Exp Reprod Med.* 2012;39(1):1-9. doi: 10.5653/cerm.2012.39.1.1. [Epub 2012 Mar 31].
     Note: Addditional footnotes related to chart built by Gye and Park:
     A   Yellon SM. **Acute 60 Hz magnetic field exposure effects on the melatonin rhythm in the pineal gland and circulation of the adult Djungarian hamster.** *J Pineal Res.* 1994;16:136–144.
     B   Stevens RG, Davis S. **The melatonin hypothesis: electric power and breast cancer.** *Environ Health Perspect.* 1996;104(Suppl 1):135–140.
     C   Sarkar S, Ali S, Behari J. **Effect of low power microwave on the mouse genome: a direct DNA analysis.** *Mutat Res.* 1994;320:141–147.
     D   Aitken RJ, Bennetts LE, Sawyer D, Wiklendt AM, King BV. **Impact of radio frequency electromagnetic radiation on DNA integrity in the male germline.** *Int J Androl.* 2005;28:171–179.
     E   Nikolova T, Czyz J, Rolletschek A, et al. **Electromagnetic fields affect transcript levels of apoptosis-related genes in embryonic stem cell-derived neural progenitor cells.** *FASEB J.* 2005;19:1686–1688.
     F   Saygin M, Caliskan S, Karahan N, Koyu A, Gumral N, Uguz A. **Testicular apoptosis and histopathological changes induced by a 2.45 GHz electromagnetic field.** *Toxicol Ind Health.* 2011;27:455–463.
     G   Lee JS, Ahn SS, Jung KC, Kim YW, Lee SK. **Effects of 60 Hz electromagnetic field exposure on testicular germ cell apoptosis in mice.** *Asian J Androl.* 2004;6:29–34.
     H   Kim YW, Kim HS, Lee JS, et al. **Effects of 60 Hz 14 microT magnetic field on the apoptosis of testicular germ cell in mice.** *Bioelectromagnetics.* 2009;30:66–72.
     I   Fabra I, Roig JV, Sancho C, Mir-Labrador J, Sempere J, García-Ferrer L. **Cocaine-induced ischemic colitis in a high-risk patient treated conservatively.** *Gastroenterol Hepatol.* 2011;34:20–23.
     J   Bernabò N, Tettamanti E, Pistilli MG, et al. **Effects of 50 Hz extremely low frequency magnetic field on the morphology and function of boar spermatozoa capacitated in vitro.** *Theriogenology.* 2007;67:801–815.
     K   Bernabò N, Tettamanti E, Russo V, et al. **Extremely low frequency electromagnetic field exposure affects fertilization outcome in swine animal model.** *Theriogenology.* 2010;73:1293–1305.
     L   Roychoudhury S, Jedlicka J, Parkanyi V, et al. **Influence of a 50 hz extra low frequency electromagnetic field on spermatozoa motility and fertilization rates in rabbits.** *J Environ Sci Health A Tox Hazard Subst Environ Eng.* 2009;44:1041–1047.
     M   Rodriguez M, Petitclerc D, Burchard JF, Nguyen DH, Block E, Downey BR. **Responses of the estrous cycle in dairy cows exposed to electric**

and magnetic fields (60 Hz) during 8-h photoperiods. *Anim Reprod Sci.* 2003;77:11–20.

N   Rodriguez M, Petitclerc D, Burchard JF, Nguyen DH, Block E. **Blood melatonin and prolactin concentrations in dairy cows exposed to 60 Hz electric and magnetic fields during 8 h photoperiods.** *Bioelectromagnetics.* 2004;25:508–515.

O   Lincoln GA, Maeda KI. **Reproductive effects of placing micro-implants of melatonin in the mediobasal hypothalamus and preoptic area in rams.** *J Endocrinol.* 1992;132:201–215.

P   Malpaux B, Daveau A, Maurice F, Gayrard V, Thiery JC. **Short-day effects of melatonin on luteinizing hormone secretion in the ewe: evidence for central sites of action in the mediobasal hypothalamus.** *Biol Reprod.* 1993;48:752–760.

Q   Jung KA, Ahn HS, Lee YS, Gye MC. **Effect of a 20 kHz sawtooth magnetic field exposure on the estrous cycle in mice.** *J Microbiol Biotechnol.* 2007;17:398–402.

R   Cecconi S, Gualtieri G, Di Bartolomeo A, Troiani G, Cifone MG, Canipari R. **Evaluation of the effects of extremely low frequency electromagnetic fields on mammalian follicle development.** *Hum Reprod.* 2000;15:2319–2325.

S   Bernabò N, Tettamanti E, Russo V, et al. **Extremely low frequency electromagnetic field exposure affects fertilization outcome in swine animal model.** *Theriogenology.* 2010;73:1293–1305

T   Borhani N, Rajaei F, Salehi Z, Javadi A. **Analysis of DNA fragmentation in mouse embryos exposed to an extremely low-frequency electromagnetic field.** *Electromagn Biol Med.* 2011;30:246–252.

U   Kowalczuk C, Robbins L, Thomas JM, Butland BK, Saunders RD. **Effects of prenatal exposure to 50 Hz magnetic fields on development in mice: I. Implantation rate and fetal development.** *Bioelectromagnetics.* 1994;15:349–361.

V   Goldhaber MK, Polen MR, Hiatt RA. **The risk of miscarriage and birth defects among women who use visual display terminals during pregnancy.** *Am J Ind Med.* 1988;13:695–706.

W   Bergqvist UO. **Video display terminals and health. A technical and medical appraisal of the state of the art.** *Scand J Work Environ Health.* 1984;10(Suppl 2):1–87.

X   Tenorio BM, Jimenez GC, Morais RN, Torres SM, Albuquerque Nogueira R, Silva Junior VA. **Testicular development evaluation in rats exposed to 60 Hz and 1 mT electromagnetic field.** *J Appl Toxicol.* 2011;31:223–230.

Y   Kowalczuk C, Robbins L, Thomas JM, Butland BK, Saunders RD. **Effects of prenatal exposure to 50 Hz magnetic fields on development in mice: I. Implantation rate and fetal development.** *Bioelectromagnetics.* 1994;15:349–361.

235 Gye MC, Park CJ. **Effect of electromagnetic field exposure on the reproductive system.** *Clin Exp Reprod Med.* 2012;39(1):1-9. doi: 10.5653/cerm.2012.39.1.1. [Epub 2012 Mar 31].

236 Guney M, Ozguner F, Oral B, Karahan N, Mungan T. **900 MHz radiofrequency-induced histopathologic changes and oxidative stress in rat endometrium: protection by vitamins E and C.** *Toxicol Ind Health.* 2007;23:411–420.

237 Özorak A, Nazıroğlu M, Çelik Ö, et al. **Wi-Fi (2.45 GHz)- and mobile phone (900 and 1800 MHz)-induced risks on oxidative stress and elements in kidney and testis of rats during pregnancy and the development of offspring.** *Biol Trace Elem Res.* 2013;156(1-3):221-229. doi: 10.1007/s12011-013-9836-z. [Epub 2013 Oct 8].

238 Saygin M, Caliskan S, Karahan N, Koyu A, Gumral N, Uguz A. **Testicular apoptosis and histopathological changes induced by a 2.45 GHz electromagnetic field.** *Toxicol Ind Health.* 2011;27(5):455-463. doi: 10.1177/0748233710389851. [Epub 2011 Feb 10].

239 Mailankot M, Kunnath AP, Javalekshmi H, Koduru B, Valsalan R. **Radio frequency electromagnetic radiation (RF–EMR) from GSM (0.9/1.8GHz) mobile phones induces oxidative stress and reduces sperm motility in rats.** *Clinics* (Sao Paulo). 2009;64(6):561-565.

240 Kesari KK, Kumar S, Nirala J, Siddiqui MH, Behari J. **Biophysical evaluation of radiofrequency electromagnetic field effects on male reproductive pattern.** *Cell Biochem Biophys.* 2013;65(2):85-96.

241 Cervellati F, Franceschetti G, Lunghi L, et al. **Effect of high-frequency electromagnetic fields on trophoblastic connexins.** *Reprod Toxicol.* 2009;28(1):59-65.

242 Herve' JC. **The connexins, part III, [editorial].** *Biochimt Biophys Acta.* 2005;1719(1-2):1-2.

     Cyr DG. **Connexins and pannexins: Coordinating cellular communication in the testis and epididymis.** *Spermatogenesis.* 2011;1(4):325-338.[Epub 2011 Oct 1].

243 La Vignera S, Condorelli RA, Vicari E, D'Agata R, Calogero AE. **Effects of the exposure to mobile phones on male reproduction: a review of the literature.** *J Androl.* 2012;33(3):350-356. doi: 10.2164/jandrol.111.014373. [Epub 2011 Jul 28].

244 Kumar S, Behari J, Sisodia R. **Impact of microwave at X-band in the aetiology of male infertility.** *Electromagn Biol Med.* 2012;31(3):223-232. doi: 10.3109/15368378.2012.700293.

245 Kesari KK, Kumar S, Behari J. **Effects of radiofrequency electromagnetic wave exposure from cellular phones on the reproductive pattern in male Wistar rats.** *Appl Biochem Biotechnol.* 2011;164(4):546-559. doi: 10.1007/s12010-010-9156-0. [Epub 2011 Jan 15].

246 Kumar S, Behari J, Sisodia R. **Influence of electromagnetic fields on reproductive system of male rats.** *Int J Radiat Biol.* 2012 Nov 13. [Epub ahead of print].

247 Reiter RJ, Tan DX, Manchester LC, et. al. **Melatonin and Reproduction Revisited.** *Biology of Reproduction.* 2009;81(3):445-456. Retrieved March 9, 2015 from: www.biolreprod.org/content/81/3/445.full

248 Magras IN, Xenos TD. **RF radiation-induced changes in the prenatal development of mice.** *Bioelectromagnetics.* 1997;18(6):455-461.

249 Gye MC, Park CJ. **Effect of electromagnetic field exposure on the reproductive system.** *Clin Exp Reprod Med.* 2012;39(1):1-9.

250 Herve' JC. **The connexins, part III, [editorial].** *Biochimt Biophys Acta.* 2005;1719(1-2):1-2.

     Laws MJ, Taylor RN, Sidell N, et al. **Gap junction communication between uterine stromal cells plays a critical role in pregnancy-associated neovascularization and embryo survival.** *Development.* 2008;135(15):2659-2668. doi: 10.1242/dev.019810. [Epub 2008 Jul 3].

251 Cervellati F, Franceschetti G, Lunghi L, et al. **Effect of high-frequency electromagnetic fields on trophoblastic connexins.** *Reprod Toxicol.* 2009;28(1):59-65.

252 Luo Q, Jiang Y, Jin M, Xu J, Huang HF. **Reprod Proteomic analysis on the alteration of protein expression in the early-stage placental villous tissue of electromagnetic fields associated with cell phone exposure.** *Sci.* 2013 Feb 18. [Epub ahead of print].

253 Bellieni CV, Pinto I, Bogi A, et al. **Exposure to electromagnetic fields from laptop use of "laptop" computers.** *Arch Environ Occup Health.* 2012;67(1):31-36. doi: 10.1080/19338244.2011.564232.

254 Ashraf El-Sayed A, Hoda S. Badr H.S., Yahia R, Salem SM, Kandil AM. **Effects of thirty minute mobile phone irradiation on morphological and physiological parameters and gene expression in pregnant rats and their fetuses.** *African Journal of Biotechnology.* 2011;10 (84):19670-19680.

255 Al-Guborya KH, Fowlerb PA, Garrel C. **The roles of cellular reactive oxygen species, oxidative stress and antioxidants in pregnancy outcomes.** *The International Journal of Biochemistry & Cell Biology.* 2010;42:1634-1650.

256 Trower B. White Paper entitled: **Wi-Fi—A Thalidomide in the Making. Who Cares?** Retrieved August 10, 2015 from: http://emfsummit.com/wp-content/ uploads/2014/10/WiFi-a-Thalidomide-in-the-making-who-cares.pdf.

257 Sekeroqu V, Akar A, Sekeroqlu ZA. **Cytotoxic and genotoxic effects of high-frequency electromagnetic fields (GSM 1800 MHz) on immature and mature rats.** *Ecotoxicol Environ Saf.* 2012;80:140-144. doi: 10.1016/j. ecoenv.2012.02.028. [Epub 2012 Mar 9].

258 Aydin B, Akar A. **Effects of a 900-MHz electromagnetic field on oxidative stress parameters in rat lymphoid organs, polymorphonuclear leukocytes and plasma.** *Arch Med Res.* 2011 May;42(4):261-267. doi: 10.1016/j. arcmed.2011.06.001.

259 Atlı Şekeroğlu Z, Akar A, Şekeroğlu V. **Evaluation of the cytogenotoxic damage in immature and mature rats exposed to 900 MHz radiofrequency electromagnetic fields.** *Int J Radiat Biol.* 2013;89(11):985-992. doi: 10.3109/09553002.2013.809170. [Epub 2013 Jun 21].

260 Li DK, Chen H, Odouli R. **Maternal exposure to magnetic fields during pregnancy in relation to the risk of asthma in offspring.** *Arch Pediatr Adolesc Med.* 2011;165(10):945-950. [Epub 2011 Aug 1]. Abstract only.

261 Li DK, Ferber JR, Odouli R, Quesenberry CP Jr. **A prospective study of in-utero exposure to magnetic fields and the risk of childhood obesity.** *Sci Rep.* 2012;2:540. [Epub 2012 Jul 27].

262 Chiu CT, Chang YH, Chen CC, Ko MC, Li CY. **Mobile phone use and health symptoms in children.** *J Formos Med Assoc.* 2014 Aug 9. pii: S0929-6646(14)00207-1. doi: 10.1016/j.jfma.2014.07.002. [Epub ahead of print].

263 Calvente I, Fernandez MF, Villalba J, Olea N, Nuñez MI. **Exposure to electromagnetic fields (non-ionizing radiation) and its relationship with childhood leukemia: a systematic review.** *Sci Total Environ.* 2010;408(16):3062-3069. doi: 10.1016/j.scitotenv.2010.03.039. [Epub 2010 May 7].

264 Salford LG, Brun AE, Eberhardt JL, Malmgren L, Persson BR. **Nerve cell damage in mammalian brain after exposure to microwaves from GSM mobile phones.** *Environ Health Perspect.* 2003;111(7):881-883; discussion A408.

265 Bas O, Odaci E, Kaplan S, Acer N, Ucok K, Colakoglu S. **900 MHz electromagnetic field exposure affects qualitative and quantitative features of hippocampal pyramidal cells in the adult female rat.** *Brain Res.* 2009;1265:178-185. [Epub 2009 Feb 20].

266 Paulraj R, Behari J. **Biochemical changes in rat brain exposed to low intensity 9.9 GHz microwave radiation.** *Cell Biochem Biophys.* 2012;63(1):97-102. doi: 10.1007/s12013-012-9344-3.

267 Motawi TK, Darwish HA, Moustafa YM, Labib MM. **Biochemical modifications and neuronal damage in brain of young and adult rats after long-term exposure to mobile phone radiations.** *Cell Biochem Biophys.* 2014;70(2):845-855. doi: 10.1007/s12013-014-9990-8.

268 Pérez-Castejón C, Pérez-Bruzón RN, Llorente M, et al. **Exposure to ELF-pulse modulated X band microwaves increases in vitro human astrocytoma cell proliferation.** *Histol Histopathol.* 2009;24(12):1551-1561.

269 Feychting M. **Mobile phones, radiofrequency fields, and health effects in children– epidemiological studies.** *Prog Biophys Mol Biol.* 2011;107(3):343-348.

270 Carlberg M, Hardell L. **On the association between glioma, wireless phones, heredity and ionising radiation.** *Pathophysiology.* 2012;19(4):243-252.

271 The Guardian - UK News website. Ratcliffe R. **Children can swipe a screen but can't use toy building blocks, teachers warn.** *The Guardian* UK news. Tuesday 15 April 2014 13.13 EDT.

272 Paul B, Saha I, Kumar S, Samim Ferdows SK, Ghose G. **Mobile phones: time to rethink and limit usage.** *Indian J Public Health.* 2015;59(1):37-41. doi: 10.4103/0019-557X.152856.

273 Krey JF, Dolmetsch RE. **Molecular mechanisms of autism: a possible role for Ca2+ signaling.** *Curr Opin Neurobiol.* 2007;17(1):112-119. [Epub 2007 Feb 1].

274 Treffert DA. **Autistic disorder 52 years later: some common sense conclusions.** Retrieved March 20, 2013 from: www.wisconsinmedicalsociety.org/ professional/savant-syndrome/resources/articles/4907-2/.

Wallis C. **New studies see a higher rate of autism: is the jump real?** *Time* Magazine website. Retrieved March 20, 2013 from: www.time.com/time/ health/article/0,8599,1927824,00.html.

Baio J. **Prevalence of Autism Spectrum Disorder Among Children Aged 8 Years — Autism and Developmental Disabilities Monitoring Network, 11 Sites, United States,** *2010 Surveillance Summaries*. March 28, 2014 / 63(SS02);1-21.

Maenner MJ, Shaw KA, Bakian AV, et al. **Prevalence and Characteristics of Autism Spectrum Disorder Among Children Aged 8 Years—Autism and Developmental Disabilities Monitoring Network, 11 Sites, United States, 2018**. MMWR Surveill Summ 2021;70(No. SS-11):1–16.

Autism Speaks Website. **Autism Statistics and Facts**. Retrieved Feb. 10, 2023 from: www.autismspeaks.org/autism-statistics-asd.

275 Osipowicz K, Bosenbark DD, Patrick KE. **Cortical changes across the autism lifespan.** *Autism Res.* 2015 Jan 28. doi: 10.1002/aur.1453. [Epub ahead of print]

276 Medicines for Mental Health website. Thompson, K. **Anosognosia.** Retrieved August 5, 2015 from: www.mentalmeds.org/articles/anosognosia.html

277 Gross RG, Grossman M. **Update on apraxia.** *Curr Neurol Neurosci Rep.* 2008;8(6):490-496.

U.S. Dept. of Health & Human Services website. No author cited. **Communication problems in children with autism spectrum disorder.** Retrieved August 5, 2015 from: ww.nidcd.nih.gov/health/voice/Pages/Communication-Problems-in-Children-with-Autism-Spectrum-Disorder.aspx

278 Razavinasab M, Moazzami K, Shabani M. **Maternal mobile phone exposure alters intrinsic electrophysiological properties of CA1 pyramidal neurons in rat offspring.** *Toxicol Ind Health*. 2014 Mar 6. [Epub ahead of print.]

279 Júnior LC, Guimarães Eda S, Musso CM, et al. **Behavior and memory evaluation of Wistar rats exposed to 1.8 GHz radiofrequency electromagnetic radiation.** *Neurol Res.* 2014;36(9):800-803. doi: 10.1179/1743132813Y.0000000276. [Epub 2014 Jan 27].

280 Narayanan SN, Kumar RS, Paval J, et al **Analysis of emotionality and locomotion in radio-frequency electromagnetic radiation exposed rats.** *Neurol Sci.* 2013;34(7):1117-1124. doi: 10.1007/s10072-012-1189-4. [Epub 2012 Sep 14].

281 Narayanan SN, Kumar RS, Potu BK, Nayak S, Bhat PG, Mailankot M. **Effect of radio-frequency electromagnetic radiations (RF-EMR) on passive avoidance behaviour and hippocampal morphology in Wistar rats.** *Ups J Med Sci.* 2010;115(2):91-96. doi: 10.3109/03009730903552661.

282 [No authors listed] **Evaluation of oxidant stress and antioxidant defense in discrete brain regions of rats exposed to 900 MHz radiation.** *Bratisl Lek Listy.* 2014;115(5):260-266.

283 Haghani M, Shabani M, Moazzami K. **Maternal mobile phone exposure adversely affects the electrophysiological properties of Purkinje neurons in rat offspring.** *Neuroscience.* 2013;250:588-598. doi: 10.1016/j. neuroscience.2013.07.049. [Epub 2013 Jul 29].

284 Fatemi SH, Aldinger KA, Ashwood P, et al. **Consensus paper: pathological role of the cerebellum in autism.** *Cerebellum.* 2012;11(3):777-807. doi: 10.1007/ s12311-012-0355-9.

285 Salmond CH, Ashburner J, Connelly A, Friston KJ, Gadian DG, Vargha-Khadem F. **The role of the medial temporal lobe in autistic spectrum disorders.** *Eur J Neurosci.* 2005;22(3):764-772.

286 Odaci E, Bas O, Kaplan S. **Effects of prenatal exposure to a 900 MHz electromagnetic field on the dentate gyrus of rats: a stereological and histopathological study.** *Brain Res.* 2008;1238:224-229. [Epub 2008 Aug 16].

Bas O, Odaci E, Mollaoglu H, Ucok K, Kaplan S. **Chronic prenatal exposure to the 900 megahertz electromagnetic field induces pyramidal cell loss in the hippocampus of newborn rats.** *Toxicol Ind Health*. 2009;25(6):377-384.

287 Banerjee A, García-Oscos F, Roychowdhury S, et al. **Impairment of cortical GABAergic synaptic transmission in an environmental rat model of autism.** *Int J Neuropsychopharmacol.* 2012;11:1-10.
Coghlan S, Horder J, Inkster B, Mendez MA, Murphy DG, Nutt DJ. **GABA system dysfunction in autism and related disorders: from synapse to symptoms.** *Neurosci Biobehav Rev.* 2012;36(9):2044-2055. doi: 10.1016/j.neubiorev.2012.07.005. [Epub 2012 Jul 25].

288 Center for Collaborative Psychiatry, Psychology, and Medicine website. Engelman DH. **Brain-behavior relationships in systems of emotion.** 2005. Retrieved March 20, 2013 from: www.collaborativepsychology.com/pdfs/article_emotion.pdf.

289 Gürkan CK, Hagerman RJ. **Targeted treatments in autism and fragile x syndrome.** *Res Autism Spectr Disord.* 2012;6(4):1311-1320.

290 Fatemi SH, Folsom TD, Reutiman TJ, Thuras PD. **Expression of GABA(B) receptors is altered in brains of subjects with autism.** *Cerebellum.* 2009;8(1):64-69. doi: 10.1007/s12311-008-0075-3.

291 Mathew J, Gangadharan G, Kuruvilla KP, Paulose CS. **Behavioral deficit and decreased GABA receptor functional regulation in the hippocampus of epileptic rats: effect of Bacopa monnieri.** *Neurochem Res.* 2011;36(1):7-16. doi: 10.1007/s11064-010-0253-9. [Epub 2010 Sep 7].

292 Krey JF, Dolmetsch RE. **Molecular mechanisms of autism: a possible role for Ca2+ signaling.** *Curr Opin Neurobiol.* 2007;17(1):112-119. [Epub 2007 Feb 1].

293 Yarlagadda A, Kaushik S, Clayton AH. **Blood-brain barrier: the role of calcium homeostasis.** *Psychiatry* (Edgmont). 2007;4(12):55-59.

294 Palmieri L, Papaleo V, Porcelli V, et al. **Altered calcium homeostasis in autism-spectrum disorders: evidence from biochemical and genetic studies of the mitochondrial aspartate/glutamate carrier AGC1.** *Mol Psychiatry.* 2010;15(1):38-52. [Epub 2008 Jul 8]. Abstract only.

295 Napolioni V, Persico AM, Porcelli V, Palmieri L. **The mitochondrial aspartate/ glutamate carrier AGC1 and calcium homeostasis: physiological links and abnormalities in autism.** *Mol Neurobiol.* 2011;44(1):83-92. [Epub 2011 Jun 21]. Abstract only.

296 Hemmings WA. **The entry into the brain of large molecules derived from dietary protein.** *Proc Roy Soc London Ser B.* 1978;200:175-192.

297 Ashwood P, Anthony A, Torrente F, Wakefield AJ. **Spontaneous mucosal lymphocyte cytokine profiles in children with autism and gastrointestinal symptoms: mucosal immune activation and reduced counter regulatory interleukin-10.** *J Clin Immunol.* 2004;24(6):664-673. Abstract only.

298 Wasilewska J, Jarocka-Cyrta E, Kaczmarski M. **Gastrointestinal abnormalities in children with autism.** *Pol Merkur Lekarski.* 2009;27(157):40-43. Abstract only.

299 Ahlsen G., Rosengren L., Belfrage M., et al. **Glial fibrillary acidic protein in the cerebrospinal fluid of children with autism and other neuropsychiatric disorders.** *Biological Psychiatry.* 1993;33:734-743.

300 Laurence JA., Fatemi SH. **Glial fibrillary acidic protein is elevated in superior frontal, parietal and cerebellar cortices of autistic subjects.** *Cerebellum.* 2005;4:206-210.

301 Rodriguez JI, Kern JK. **Evidence of microglial activation in autism and its possible role in brain underconnectivity.** *Neuron Glia Biol.* 2011;7(2-4):205-213. doi: 10.1017/S1740925X12000142. [Epub 2012 Jul 6].
Herbert MR, Sage C. **Autism and EMF? Plausibility of a pathophysiological link - Part I.** *Pathophysiology.* 2013;20(3):191-209. doi:10.1016/j.pathophys.2013.08.001. [Epub 2013 Oct 4].
Herbert MR, Sage C. **Autism and EMF? Plausibility of a pathophysiological link - Part II.** *Pathophysiology.* 2013;20(3):211-234. doi:10.1016/j.pathophys.2013.08.002. [Epub 2013 Oct 8].

302 Cotswolds Journal website. Mason V. **Parents of schoolgirl Jenny Fry are campaigning to have Wi-Fi restricted in schools following her death.** Retrieved December 1, 2015 from: www.cotswoldjournal.co.uk/news/14102769.Parents_of_schoolgirl_Jenny_Fry_are_campaigning_to_have_WiFi_restricted_in_schools_following_her_death/?ref=ebmpn

303 *The Atlantic* website. Rosin H. **The Silicon Valley Suicides: Why are so many kids with bright prospects killing themselves in Palo Alto?** December 2015. Retrieveved February 7, 2016 from: www.theatlantic.com/magazine/archive/2015/12/the-silicon-valley-suicides/413140/

304 ABC Science Online. Salleh, A. **Suicides linked to electromagnetic radiation.** Wednesday, 23 August 2000. Retrieved December 25, 2015 from: www.abc.net.au/science/articles/2000/08/23/166348.htm.

305 van Wijngaarden E, Savitz DA, Kleckner RC, Cai J, Loomis D. **Exposure to electromagnetic fields and suicide among electric utility workers: a nested case-control study.** *West J Med.* 2000;173(2): 94–100.

306 Wilson BW. **Chronic exposure to ELF fields may induce depression.** *Bioelectromagnetics.* 1988;9:195-205.

307 Perlis ML, Grandner MA, Chakravorty S, Bernert RA, Brown GK, Thase ME. **Suicide and sleep: Is it a bad thing to be awake when reason sleeps?** *Sleep Med Rev.* 2015;29:101-107. doi: 10.1016/j.smrv.2015.10.003. [Epub ahead of print]

   Bernert RA, Nadorff MR. **Sleep Disturbances and Suicide Risk,** *Sleep Med Clin.* 2015;10(1):35-39. doi: 10.1016/j.jsmc.2014.11.004. [Epub 2014 Dec 17.]

   Pigeon WR, Pinquart M, Conner K. **Meta-analysis of sleep disturbance and suicidal thoughts and behaviors.** *J Clin Psychiatry.* 2012;73(9):e1160-7. doi: 10.4088/JCP.11r07586.

308 Luscher B, Shen Q, Sahir N. **The GABAergic deficit hypothesis of major depressive disorder.** *Mol Psychiatry.* 2011;16(4):383-406. doi: 10.1038/mp.2010.120. [Epub 2010 Nov 16.]

   Luscher B, Fuchs T. **GABAergic control of depression-related brain states.** *Adv Pharmacol.* 2015;73:97-144. doi: 10.1016/bs.apha.2014.11.003. [Epub 2015 Jan 14.]

   Sanacora G, Saricicek A. **GABAergic contributions to the pathophysiology of depression and the mechanism of antidepressant action.** *CNS Neurol Disord Drug Targets.* 2007;6(2):127-140.

   Kasa K, Otsuki S, Yamamoto M, Sato M, Kuroda H, Ogawa N. **Cerebrospinal fluid gamma-aminobutyric acid and homovanillic acid in depressive disorders.** *Biol Psychiatry.* 1982;17(8):877-883.

309 Honig A, Bartlett JR, Bouras N, Bridges PK. **Amino acid levels in depression: A preliminary investigation.** J. *Psychiatr. Res.* 1988;22:159–164.

310 Smiley JF, Hackett TA, Bleiwas C, et al. **Reduced GABA neuron density in auditory cerebral cortex of subjects with major depressive disorder.** *J Chem Neuroanat.* 2015 Dec 12. pii: S0891-0618(15)00092-7. doi: 10.1016/j.jchemneu.2015.10.008. [Epub ahead of print]

311 Thomée S, Härenstam A, Hagberg M. **Mobile phone use and stress, sleep disturbances, and symptoms of depression among young adults--a prospective cohort study.** *BMC Public Health.* 2011;11:66. doi: 10.1186/1471-2458-11-66.

312 Thomée S, Härenstam A, Hagberg M. **Computer use and stress, sleep disturbances, and symptoms of depression among young adults--a prospective cohort study.** *BMC Psychiatry.* 2012;12:176. doi: 10.1186/1471-244X-12-176.

313 Unpublished material, received via personal communication from Debbie Fry, Jenny Fry's mother. Dated: December 1, 2015.

314 Manzetti S, Johansson O. **Global electromagnetic toxicity and frequency-induced diseases: Theory and short overview.** *Pathophysiology.* 2012 Jun;19(3):185-91. doi: 10.1016/j.pathophys.2012.04.009. [Epub 2012 Jul 27].

315 Milham S. **Historical evidence that electrification cause the 20th century epidemic of diseases of civilization.** *Medical Hypotheses.* 2010 Feb;74(2):337-45. doi: 10.1016/j.mehy.2009.08.032. [Epub 2009 Sep 11].
316 CDC (U.S.) website. **Leading causes of death.** Retrieved Aug. 24, 2015 from www.cdc.gov/nchs/fastats/leading-causes-of-death.htm
317 Talamanca IF, Giliberti C, Salerno S. **[Cell phones: health risks and prevention].** *Ann Ig.* 2012;24(1):3-23.
     Paul B, Saha I, Kumar S, Samim Ferdows SK, Ghose G. **Mobile phones: time to rethink and limit usage.** *Indian J Public Health.* 2015;59(1):37-41. doi: 10.4103/0019-557X.152856.
     Kundi M, Hardell L, Sage C, Sobel E. **Electromagnetic fields and the precautionary principle.** *Environ Health Perspect.* 2009;117(11):A484-485; author reply A485. doi: 10.1289/ehp.0901111
318 Grigor'ev IuG. **[The electromagnetic fields of cellular phones and the health of children and of teenagers (the situation requiring to take an urgent measure)].** *Radiats Biol Radioecol.* 2005;45(4):442-450.
319 Sagi O, Sadetzki S. **[Determining health policy for sensible mobile phone use-- current world status].** *Harefuah.* 2011;150(3):216-220,306.
320 Gee D. **Late Lessons from Early Warnings: Towards realism and precaution with EMF?** *Pathophysiology.* 2009;16(2-3):217-231. doi: 10.1016/j. pathophys.2009.01.004. [Epub 2009 May 21].
321 Johansson O. Dämvik M. **Health risk assessment of electromagnetic fields: a conflict between the precautionary principle and environmental medicine methodology.** *Rev Environ Health.* 2010;25(4):325-333.
322 United Nations Organization for Education, Science and Culture (UNESCO) website. **The Precautionary Principle.** By the World Commission on the Ethics of Scientific Knowledge and Technology (COMEST). Retrieved August 18, 2015 from: http://unesdoc.unesco.org/images/0013/001395/139578e.pdf
323 Zinelis SA. **The precautionary principle: radiofrequency exposures from mobile telephones and base stations.** *Environ Health Perspect.* 2010;118(1):A16; author reply A16-17.
     Dolan M, Rowley J. **The precautionary principle in the context of mobile phone and base station radiofrequency exposures.** *Environ Health Perspect.* 2009;117(9):1329-1332. doi: 10.1289/ehp.0900727. [Epub 2009 May 18].
324 CBS Los Angeles website. Wireless Broadband-Equipped 'Smartpole' Streetlight Installed In Hollywood. Retrieved February 15, 2016 from: http://losange-les.cbslocal.com/2015/11/05/wireless-broadband-equipped-smartpole-street-light-installed-in-hollywood/
     Google website. Project Loon: Balloon-powered Internet For Everyone. Retrieved February 15, 2016 from: www.google.com/loon/
325 Johansson O. **Electrohypersensitivity: state-of-the-art of a functional impairment.** *Electromagn Biol Medicine.* 2006;25: 245–258. ISSN 1536-8378 print DOI: 10.1080/15368370601044150
326 Harmanci H, Emre M, Gurvit H, et al. **Risk factors for Alzheimer disease: a population-based case-control study in Istanbul, Turkey.** *Alzheimer Dis Assoc Disord.* 2003;17(3):139-145.
327 Havas M. **Dirty electricity elevates blood sugar among electrically sensitive diabetics and may explain brittle diabetes.** *Electromagn Biol Med.* 2008;27(2):135-146. doi: 10.1080/15368370802072075.
328 Joseph W, Frei P, Roösli M, et al. **Comparison of personal radio frequency electromagnetic field exposure in different urban areas across Europe.** *Environ Res.* 2010;110(7):658-663. doi: 10.1016/j.envres.2010.06.009.
329 Lewicka M, Henrykowska GA, Pacholski K, Szczęsny A, Dziedziczak-Buczyńska M, Buczyński A. **The impact of electromagnetic radiation of different parameters on platelet oxygen metabolism - in vitro studies.** *Adv Clin Exp Med.* 2015;24(1):31-35. doi: 10.17219/acem/38169.

330 Imge EB, Kiliçoğlu B, Devrim E, Cetin R, Durak I. **Effects of mobile phone use on brain tissue from the rat and a possible protective role of vitamin C - a preliminary study.** *Int J Radiat Biol.* 2010;86(12):1044-1049. doi: 10.3109/09553002.2010.501838. [Epub 2010 Aug 10].

331 Al-Damegh MA. **Rat testicular impairment induced by electromagnetic radiation from a conventional cellular telephone and the protective effects of the antioxidants vitamins C and E.** *Clinics* (Sao Paulo). 2012;67(7):785-792.

332 Guney M, Ozguner F, Oral B, Karahan N, Mungan T. **900 MHz radiofrequency-induced histopathologic changes and oxidative stress in rat endometrium: protection by vitamins E and C.** *Toxicol Ind Health.* 2007;23:411–420.

333 Ozguner F, Altinbas A, Ozaydin M, et. al. **Mobile phone-induced myocardial oxidative stress: protection by a novel antioxidant agent caffeic acid phenethyl ester.** *Toxicol Ind Health.* 2005;21(9):223-230.

334 Akyol S, Ugurcu V, Altuntas A, Hasgul R, Cakmak O, Akyol O. **Caffeic acid phenethyl ester as a protective agent against nephrotoxicity and/or oxidative kidney damage: a detailed systematic review.** *Scientific World Journal.* 2014;2014:561971. doi:10.1155/2014/561971. [Epub 2014 Jun 3].

335 Ceyhan AM, Akkaya VB, Güleçol ŞC, Ceyhan BM, Özgüner F, Chen W. **Protective effects of β-glucan against oxidative injury induced by 2.45-GHz electromagnetic radiation in the skin tissue of rats.** *Arch Dermatol Res.* 2012;304(7):521-527. doi: 10.1007/s00403-012-1205-9. [Epub 2012 Jan 12].

336 Ilhan A, Gurel A, Armutcu F, et al. **Ginkgo biloba prevents mobile phone-induced oxidative stress in rat brain.** *Clin Chim Acta.* 2004;340(1-2):153-162.

337 Environmental Working Group (EWG). EWG website. **EWG's 2015 Shopper's Guide to Pesticides in Produce™.** Retrieved June 6, 2015 at: www.ewg.org/foodnews/?gclid=CNPjk_bn_sUCFQesaQodW2wAOA.

338 Genuis SJ, Lipp CT. **Electromagnetic hypersensitivity: fact or fiction?** *Sci Total Environ.* 2012;414:103-112. [Epub 2011 Dec 5].

339 Baliatsas C, Van Kamp I, Lebret E, Rubin GJ. **Idiopathic environmental intolerance attributed to electromagnetic fields (IEI-EMF): a systematic review of identifying criteria.** *BMC Public Health.* 2012;12:643. doi: 10.1186/1471-2458-12-643.

340 Tuengler A, von Klitzing L. **Hypothesis on how to measure electromagnetic hypersensitivity.** *Electromagn Biol Med.* 2013 Jan 9. [Epub ahead of print].

341 Hänninen O, Huttunen P, Ekman R. **Electromagnetic irradiation exposure and its bioindication-an overview.** *J Environ Sci* (China). 2011;23(9):1409-1414.

342 Harvard School of Public Health website. Datz T. **Autism has high costs to U.S. society.** Retrieved March 20, 2013 from: http://archive.sph.harvard.edu/press-releases/2006-releases/press04252006.html.

343 Salford L, Brun A, Eberhardt J, Malmgren L, Persson BR. **Nerve cell damages in mammalian brain due to microwaves. Foundations of Bioelectromagnetics: Towards a New Rationale for Risk Assessment and Management.** Sponsored by the International Commission for Electromagnetic Safety, Italian Government Worker Safety Program, and Ente Zona in Venice, Italy. December 17, 2007. Retrieved September 18, 2015 from: www.icems.eu/docs/venice/6th_Workshop_Salford.pdf

344 CDC website (U.S.). **Frequently Asked Questions about Cell Phones and Your Health.** Retrieved August 8, 2015 from: www.cdc.gov/nceh/radiation/cell_phones._FAQ.html

345 Statista website. **Forecast number of mobile devices worldwide from 2020 to 2025 (in billions).** Retrieved Jan 27, 2023 from www.statista.com/statistics/245501/multiple-mobile-device-ownership-worldwide/

346 Firstenberg A. *The Invisible Rainbow: The History of Electricity and Life.* Chelsea Green Publishing; 2020.

Index

About the Authors

Elizabeth Plourde, C.L.S., NCMP, Ph.D.
Clinical Laboratory Scientist
NAMS Certified Menopause Practitioner
Medical Researcher
Health Coach
Author

International lecturer and author of health books, Dr. Plourde is a licensed Clinical Laboratory Scientist (CLS) and *North American Menopause Society Certified Menopause Practitioner, whose career included working with cutting-edge cancer and DNA medical research laboratories. The author's well-rounded education and professional expertise provided the background necessary to research the scientific and medical literature to compile this vital-to-know information in an understandable format.

Her 30-years of research and expertise in the fields of health have resulted in presentations on numerous network news and radio shows, and medical conferences.

Marcus Plourde, Ph.D.
New Voice Publications

As Editor-in-Chief of New Voice Publications, Dr. Plourde has spent two decades conducting medical research. New Voice offers books, educational services, and consulting that promote good health and treat the root causes of disease, rather than treating symptoms. In the process of editing and publishing cutting-edge alternative and holistic health books, it became apparent that consumers are not receiving the best health care

available from *standard of care* medicine. It is New Voice Publication's mission to provide the educational resources consumers need to become their own advocates and take active roles in their health care choices.